THE LAUREL-LEAF LI-BRARY brings together under a single imprint outstanding works of fiction and non-fiction particularly suitable for young adult readers, both in and out of the classroom. The series should also prove of great value to the general reader in search of knowledge, instruction and pleasure.

M. Jerry Weiss, Professor of Education at Jersey City State College, has long been active in the National Council of Teachers of English and the International Reading Association. He is the author of several textbooks and the general editor of the Laurel-Leaf Library.

MAN and WAR

edited and introduced by
M. JERRY WEISS

Contents

PART THREE. THE EFFECTS OF WAR

INTRODUCTION

This book is designed to provoke thought and discussion on one of man's greatest problems—war. Through such study and interchange, man may better realize the nature of the crisis surrounding him today and may be in a better position to determine the action necessary to preserve both freedom and human life.

It is difficult to explain what war really is, especially to those who have never fought a battle or felt the effects of bombings on their homes. Yet we all know that in this century alone mankind has produced two world wars, a Korean conflict, a cold war, and a Cuban crisis that could have led to the outbreak of all-out nuclear war.

On Monday evening, October 22, 1962, President John F. Kennedy addressed this nation in a most somber manner on the danger of the Soviet missile bases being established in Cuba. The following quotations from the President's speech appeared in *The New York Times* the following day.

This Government as promised has maintained the closest surveillance of the Soviet military build-up on the island of Cuba.

Within the past week unmistakable evidence has

established the fact that a series of offensive missile sites is now in preparation on that imprisoned island.

The purpose of these bases can be none other than to provide a nuclear strike capability against the Western hemisphere. . . .

The characteristics of these new missile sites indicate two distinct types of installations. Several of them include medium-range ballistic missiles capable of carrying a nuclear warhead for a distance of more that 1,000 miles. . . .

Additional sites not yet completed appear to be designed for intermediate-range ballistic missiles capable of traveling more than twice as far, and thus capable of striking most of the major cities in the Western hemisphere ranging as far north as Hudson Bay, Canada, and as far south as Lima, Peru. . . .

Neither the United States of America nor the world community of nations can tolerate deliberate deception and offensive threats on the part of any nation, large or small. We no longer live in a world where only the actual firing of weapons represents a sufficient challenge to a nation's security to constitute maximum peril.

Nuclear weapons are so destructive and ballistic missiles are so swift that any substantially increased possibility of their use or any sudden change in their deployment may well be regarded as a definite threat to peace. . . .

The nineteen thirties taught us a clear lesson. Aggressive conduct, if allowed to go unchecked and unchallenged, ultimately leads to war.

This nation is opposed to war. We are also true to our word.

Our unswerving objective, therefore, must be to

prevent the use of these missiles against this or any other country. . . .

Our policy has been one of patience and restraint, as befits a peaceful and powerful nation which leads a worldwide alliance. . . .

We will not prematurely or unnecessarily risk the course of worldwide nuclear war in which even the fruits of victory would be ashes in our mouth, but neither will we shrink from that risk at any time it must be faced. . . .

My fellow citizens, let no one doubt that this is a difficult and dangerous effort on which we have set out. No one can foresee precisely what course it will take, or what cost or casualties will be incurred.

Many months of sacrifice and self-discipline lie ahead, months in which both our patience and our will will be tested. Months in which many threats and denunciations will keep us aware of our dangers. But the greatest danger of all would be to do nothing. . . .

The cost of freedom is always high, but Americans have always paid it.

And one path we shall never choose, and that is the path of surrender, or submission.

Our goal is not the victory of might, but the vindication of right; not peace at the expense of freedom, but both peace and freedom here in this hemisphere, and, we hope, around the world.

This nation felt the shock of a possible World War III. Young men in the reserves of our nation's armed forces were alerted to stand by for recall to active duty. It was a week of news-watching, tension, and grave concern. Radio, television, and the newspapers reported on a maritime quarantine around Cuba and hinted at a military build-up in Key West, Florida. The world watched the continued military missile build-up inside Cuba.

What would war mean? Were we right to quarantine Cuba? Demonstrations attacking the President's stand broke out on city streets and on college campuses. Many praised the President and held that his action was long overdue.

This is today. But history and literature have long recorded the grim story of man's wars and of their stirrings. In an age that has seen so much progress in combating disease and in harnessing nature's forces to help mankind, though, it would seem that the threat of all-out destruction could never arise.

Don't we know enough about war to prevent it?

It is obvious that we should be able to say yes. But can we?

Only a few years ago I took a neighborhood friend, a high school junior, to see a college theater presentation of *The Diary of Anne Frank*. We were very much impressed with this tragic tale of Nazi persecution. When we came out of the theater, my friend assured me that he had enjoyed the performance. He went on to ask if such things had actually happened. I asked him if he had studied World War II or read about Nazism in his history classes. He told me that his instructor had touched on the subject briefly. "We had spent so much time studying the earlier periods of history that we had just a few days left to study the problems of World War II and today."

From this experience I have learned that it is not an easy task to help each other see the relation of the past to the present and to the future. But it is important that all of us see war for what it is. Basically, we must understand three phases of war: (1) why men fight;

(2) men in action; (3) the effects of war. This explains
the divisions of this book.

It is now apparent to the world that this country was
ready to answer the President's call to arms. This was
not the first time men had to be ready to defend their
freedom and their beliefs. In Part One, Dr. Benjamin
Keen points out how war and its causes have changed
throughout the centuries of history. We learn why men
will risk total destruction for the preservation of their
way of life and freedom.

In this setting we might take another look at such
important documents as "The Declaration of Independence," "The American Crisis," and Franklin D.
Roosevelt's "War Message to Congress." In reading
these, perhaps we can see how painful it is for any
leader to commit his nation to battle.

In Part Two we begin to look at men, their women,
their families, their nations engaged in action. Stephen
Crane has immortalized the action on the front lines.
He reminds us that the fighting man is not only brave
but also frightened.

Whitman, Crane, and Shapiro show us through their
poems the changing values of those involved in war.
The call to arms interrupts life's normal course of
peace and work and play. Even a beautiful full moon
can become an enemy and give away a soldier's position. Columns and columns of soldiers crossing a
bridge present a spectacle that is patriotic but also
grim, for many march their last few miles alive.

There are selections describing famous battles and
other events that have left indelible scars on individual and nation alike.

Part Three reminds us that war leaves its mark on
every level of human existence. War is physical and
emotional. The stories of Dos Passos and Garland

vividly emphasize these points. Statues, monuments,
brass plates and cemetery markers commemorate those
brave men who died for their country, but the writers
who record these historic occasions and dedications
challenge us to learn to end all wars, so that these men
will not have died in vain. As nations now reconstruct
themselves from their ashes and debris, will they not
realize the futility of men's need to kill each other?

Walt Whitman stabs deep into the memories of
many with "Come Up From The Fields Father."
Norman Corwin forces mankind to answer his soldier's
question, "Will it happen again?" Michihiko Hachiya's
Hiroshima Diary selection is a grim reminder of the
effects of nuclear war on a nation.

There has been progress, if only in the means to
learn of man and of his wars. A chronology of wars is
of little value if we can't see beyond it to the horrible
folly of any war whatever in our present or our future.

This book is just the beginning of a study of man
and war. Many other sources of information are
available to help us understand the problems pre-
sented by these writers and by the discussions that will
result from reading them. Through such discussion
may come a deeper appreciation of peace, and of
Benjamin Franklin's telling words: "There never was a
good war or a bad peace."

—M. JERRY WEISS

PART ONE

WHY MEN FIGHT

WHY MEN FIGHT

BENJAMIN KEEN

War, the deadly issue of our time, is one of the oldest social institutions. Cynics, pointing to war's ancient pedigree, exclaim: "There have always been wars, there will always be wars; you can't change human nature." History does not justify this pessimism. Long life is no warrant of immortality. Cannibalism, human sacrifice, and slavery were all institutions of venerable antiquity and were all regarded as fully compatible with "human nature." Yet in the course of man's cultural advance each became an economic and moral anachronism that passed, or was driven, from the face of the earth.

Is man's tendency to warfare an instinct, part of his "nature"? Even if we concede the existence of a combative "instinct" in man, of a need for challenge and struggle—and this is a very large concession—clearly there are better outlets for such an "instinct" than organized warfare. Long ago William James proposed that these supposed needs of our being be channeled into a struggle against man's ancient enemies: Nature, sickness, poverty. He called such a program of struggle "the moral equivalent of war."

Organized warfare, in any case, is not an instinctive

activity. It is an elaborate cultural complex arising from the real or supposed clash of interests of human groups; its motives, forms, and intensity vary with the way men make their living and organize themselves socially and politically in different times and places.

Contrary to a widely held opinion, warfare among "savages" is a relatively trivial and infrequent occurrence. Economic factors, so important in the wars of civilized men, rank low among the motives for warfare of true primitives. Hereditary feuds, the desire to avenge real or fancied injuries, rank high among these motives. Amerigo Vespucci, who made voyages of discovery to South America in 1499 and 1501, could not understand why the Brazilian Indians made war on each other, since "they held no private property or sovereignty of empire and kingdoms and did not know any such thing as lust for possession—that is, pillaging or a desire to rule—which appear to me to be the causes of wars and of every disorderly act. When we requested them to state the cause, they did not know how to give any other cause than that this curse upon them began in ancient times and they sought to avenge the deaths of their forefathers." Much the same principle of reciprocity was expressed in 1933 by an old Comanche Indian whose grandson had been killed in France in 1918 and who voiced a desire to scalp a young anthropologist "because he looks like a German."

Matters change when society reaches the settled agricultural stage of development. Systematic war now becomes profitable, since the conquered are capable of producing more food and goods than they must consume to live. Now arise empires which apply military power for purposes of economic exploitation. The Assyrian, Egyptian, and Roman Empires, in the Old World, the Aztec and Inca Empires in the New, are excellent examples of such "plunder empires." Claims of divine favor or a divine mission provided a convenient sanction for these ancient imperialisms. The Aztecs, for example, proclaimed that the sun, who brought victory to the Aztec banners, must be nourished with the blood of sacrificial victims taken in battle, without which the Giver of Life would succumb. Thus "war led to sacrifice and sacrifice led back to war, in ever-widening circles."

War, it might be said, was the normal condition of feudal society. Economic advantage in the form of the right to exploit the labor of serfs or to tax commerce, or in the form of naked pillage and plunder, was the primary motive of the innumerable wars of medieval times. Despite the immense power of the Church and the piety of the times, religious factors played a relatively small part in the motives of feudal warfare. Even the Crusades, although largely inspired by Papal concern over the Moslem advance in the Middle East, were not exclusively a holy war. Indeed, a contemporary observer wrote that "only a few could be found who were actuated by a holy purpose." Indiscriminate pillage of Christian and infidel towns alike accompanied the march of many Crusaders.

The phrase "God, gold, and glory" has been used to characterize the motives of the Spanish Conquistadors who overthrew the great Indian empires of Mexico and Peru at the opening of the sixteenth century. It is probably safe to assume, however, that of this trinity of motives the second was uppermost in the minds of most. For this belief we have the authority of the grizzled old Conquistador and historian Oviedo y Valdes, writing to a would-be conqueror: "Do not say that you are going to the Indies to serve the king and to employ your time as a brave man and an *hidalgo* should; for you know that the truth is just the opposite; you are going solely because you want to have a larger fortune than your father and your neighbors."

Much the same point, perhaps, could be made concerning the so-called Religious Wars that made the period 1500-1650 among the bloodiest in European history. Religion unquestionably colored these conflicts and lent conviction and ardor to soldiers who fought and died for the dogmas of predestination and free will. Historians, however, see a complex blend of economic, political, and religious factors underlying these struggles. Indeed, in many cases religion was only a mask for the economic and political interests of self-seeking rulers and nobles who changed their religion as lightly as their dress.

The great commercial and dynastic wars of the seventeenth and eighteenth centuries exhibit the motive of self-interest in its most naked form. As for the common soldiers who took part in these heroic butcheries, the sufficient reasons for their involvement were the command of the prince, the strong arms of impressment gangs, or the desperate poverty that drove many to accept the paltry wage of military service.

The American Revolution opened a new chapter in the history of the causes for which men fight. No doubt the Revolution expressed the aspiration of the American middle class to be free from the restraints of English mercantilism. But the Revolution was more than this: it was the first great struggle for national liberation and democratic self-rule, ideals that reverberated with the sound of thunder in the Declaration of Independence. The fire lit by the American revolutionaries was passed on to France and there kindled an even greater flame. The dynamic force of nationalism, joined to the ideals of republican liberty, social reform, and internationalism, inspired the victorious armies of the French Revolution. Under Napoleon, the icy egotist who had only contempt for "ideology," the liberating passion of the French soldier degenerated into a worship of imperial grandeur and glory, into lust for pillage and plunder. But the constructive nationalism of the American and French Revolutions lived on in the European liberal revolutions of 1830 and 1848, and found perhaps its last great expression in Europe in the romantic enterprise of Garibaldi and his *camicie rosse,* the "red shirts," aimed at the liberation and unification of Italy.

The titanic conflict to which we in the United States give the name of the Civil War illustrates the frequent complexity of the motives for which men fight. Charles Beard was undoubtedly correct in viewing the war as a struggle between rival economic systems; it was in fact a conflict between the capitalist free labor economy of the North and a Southern plantation economy based on slave labor. However, these hostile economic systems in turn generated diverse notions concerning the morality and justice of slavery, the nature of the Union, and other matters. The power of these ideas over the minds of men, joined in many cases to youthful bravado and longing for excitement and glory, helps to explain the outpouring of volunteers both North and South. To be sure, as the long cruel war dragged on, weariness and defeatism spread, many began to suspect that the contest was "a rich man's war and a poor man's fight," and both sides felt compelled to resort to the draft.

As the nineteenth century drew to its close intensified economic rivalry among the great powers led to a race for colonies, regarded as indispensable sources of raw materials and outlets for the surplus capital and goods produced by the new giant industries. Each nation developed elaborate arguments to justify its own imperialism and bolster the morale of its troops when fighting sordid colonial wars. Not only national honor and economic need were invoked, but the argument of altruism. Kipling called upon the English people to "take up the White Man's Burden" and civilize "your new-caught, sullen peoples, half-devil and half-child." French imperialists proclaimed that France had a *mission civilisatrice* in Africa, and German colonists that they had a mission to spread German *Kultur* among the lesser breeds without the law. President McKinley declared, as a reason for annexing the Philippine Islands, that "there was nothing left for us to do but to take them all, and to educate the Filipinos, and uplift and Christianize them as our fellow-men for whom Christ also died." Intoxicated by jingoism and notions of race supremacy, the soldiers of these nations gaily embarked on wars that often involved the use of torture and other brutalities against weak native peoples.

World War I found the majority of the populations and armies of the warring states under the influence of an exaggerated patriotism. Each people tended to picture enemy governments as crafty aggressors and its own government as a champion of peace and national independence. Even the strong Socialist parties, with few exceptions, abandoned internationalism and gave unconditional support to their respective governments. Only later, as the war settled into a bloody stalemate, and particularly after exposure of secret prewar treaties by which lands and peoples were divided as if they were so many cheeses, did antiwar sentiment grow among the belligerents.

In the United States, Wilson's lofty rhetoric and Allied propaganda helped to convince the American people that the struggle in Europe was one between darkness and light, barbarism and civilization. German submarine attacks causing loss of American lives as well as property appeared sufficient cause for intervention. Few were aware of underlying factors: the Anglo-American Entente in the making since the turn of the century and the heavy United States economic stake in an Allied victory, among others. Later, in the cold gray dawn of the post-Versailles period, matters appeared in a different light. The War bore a rich literary harvest expressing soldierly disillusionment: John Dos Passos, *Soldiers Three;* Henri Barbusse, *Le Feu;* Andreas Latzko, *Men in War,* are three examples.

The War that was to end all war proved to be the

seedbed of the greatest war in history. Terrified by the
spread of Communist ideology as a result of the
Russian Revolution, and determined to redraw the
map of the world in their own favor, powerful groups
in the defeated and not-so-victorious countries set up
right-wing dictatorships that simultaneously stifled
democracy at home and prepared to launch wars of
conquest abroad. To win their peoples over to a
program of war, the rulers of Germany, Italy, and
Japan fed them a heady brew compounded of mili-
tarism, race supremacy, and a "divine mission" to rule
the world. The dreams of the warmakers ended in the
smoking inferno that was Berlin in May, 1945, in the
mushroom clouds over Hiroshima and Nagasaki in
August of the same year. In the wake of World War II
came a vast popular reaction against capitalism and
imperialism; Communism spread over large areas and
colonial revolts broke out in even greater areas of Asia
and Africa. In large measure, these wars of national
liberation were children of the American and French
Revolutions, but their frequent Socialist tinge reflected
some influence of the Russian Revolution.

The dominant feature of the present world scene is
the division of the earth into two great power blocs,
each headed by a colossus armed with the power to
destroy most life and all civilization in the territory of
the other, with the rest of the world seeking to maintain a precarious neutrality. The peoples of the world
fearfully watch the United States and the Soviet Union
as they brandish their atomic weapons. By a supreme
irony, the progress of science has made it possible for
war to end civilization even as that progress has made

quite pointless all the disputes wars were fought over in the past. Science has put plenty within the reach of all the world's peoples; the old disputes for possession of the most fruitful territory, for sources of raw materials, have lost their meaning. Whether mankind will learn this lesson in time, or whether it will be destroyed by its own creation, war, is the crucial question.

THE DECLARATION OF INDEPENDENCE

When in the Course of human events, it becomes necessary for one people to dissolve the political bands which have connected them with another, and to assume among the powers of the earth, the separate and equal station to which the Laws of Nature and of Nature's God entitle them, a decent respect to the opinions of mankind requires that they should declare the causes which impel them to the separation.——— We hold these truths to be self-evident, that all men are created equal, that they are endowed by their Creator with certain unalienable Rights, that among these are Life, Liberty and the pursuit of Happiness.— That to secure these rights, Governments are instituted among Men, deriving their just powers from the consent of the governed,—that whenever any Form of Government becomes destructive of these ends, it is the Right of the People to alter or to abolish it, and to institute new Government, laying its foundation on such principles and organizing its powers in such form, as to them shall seem most likely to effect their Safety and Happiness. Prudence, indeed, will dictate that Governments long established should not be changed for light and transient causes; and accordingly all experience hath shewn, that mankind are more disposed to suffer, while evils are sufferable, than to right themselves by abolishing the forms to which they are accustomed. But when a long train of abuses and usurpations, pursuing invariably the same Object, evinces a design to reduce them under absolute Despotism, it is their right, it is their duty, to throw off such Government, and to provide new Guards for their future security.—Such has been the patient sufferance of these Colonies; and such is now the necessity which constrains them to alter their former Systems of Government. The history of the present King of Great Britain is a history of repeated injuries and usurpations, all having in direct object the establishment of an absolute Tyranny over these States. To prove this, let Facts be submitted to a candid world. ———He has refused his Assent to Laws, the most wholesome and necessary for the public good.———He has forbidden his Governors to pass Laws of immediate and pressing importance, unless suspended in their operation till his Assent should be obtained; and when so suspended, he has utterly neglected to attend to them.———He has refused to pass other Laws for the accommodation of large districts of people, unless those people would relinquish the right of Representation in the Legislature, a right inestimable to them and formidable to tyrants only.———He has called together legislative bodies at places unusual, uncomfortable, and distant from the depository of their public Records, for the sole purpose of fatiguing them into compliance with his measures.———He has dissolved Representative Houses repeatedly, for opposing with manly firmness

his invasions on the rights of the people.———He has refused for a long time, after such dissolutions, to cause
others to be elected; whereby the Legislative powers, in-
capable of Annihilation, have returned to the People at
large for their exercise; the State remaining in the
mean time exposed to all the dangers of invasion from
without, and convulsions within.———He has endeavoured to prevent the population of these States;
for that purpose obstructing the Laws for Naturaliza-
tion of Foreigners; refusing to pass others to encourage
their migrations hither, and raising the conditions of
new Appropriations of Lands.———He has obstructed
the Administration of Justice, by refusing his Assent
to Laws for establishing Judiciary powers.———He has
made Judges dependent on his Will alone, for the
tenure of their offices, and the amount and payment
of their salaries.———He has erected a multitude of
New Offices, and sent hither swarms of Officers to
harass our people, and eat out their substance.———He
has kept among us, in times of peace, Standing Armies
without the Consent of our legislatures.———He has
affected to render the Military independent of and
superior to the Civil power.———He has combined
with others to subject us to a jurisdiction foreign to
our constitution, and unacknowledged by our laws;
giving his Assent to their Acts of pretended Legisla-
tion:—For Quartering large bodies of armed troops
among us:—For protecting them, by a mock Trial,
from punishment for any Murders which they should
commit on the Inhabitants of these States:—For cutting
off our Trade with all parts of the world;—For im-
posing Taxes on us without our Consent:—For de-

priving us in many cases, of the benefits of Trial by Jury:—For transporting us beyond Seas to be tried for pretended offences:—For abolishing the free System of English Laws in a neighbouring Province, establishing therein an Arbitrary government, and enlarging its Boundaries so as to render it at once an example and fit instrument for introducing the same absolute rule into these Colonies:—For taking away our Charters, abolishing our most valuable Laws, and altering fundamentally the Forms of our Governments:—For suspending our own Legislatures, and declaring themselves invested with power to legislate for us in all cases whatsoever.—He has abdicated Government here, by declaring us out of his Protection and waging War against us:—He has plundered our seas, ravaged our Coasts, burnt our towns, and destroyed the lives of our people. —He is at this time transporting large Armies of foreign Mercenaries to compleat the works of death, desolation and tyranny, already begun with circumstances of Cruelty & perfidy scarcely paralleled in the most barbarous ages, and totally unworthy the Head of a civilized nation.—He has constrained our fellow Citizens taken Captive on the high Seas to bear Arms against their Country, to become the executioners of their friends and Brethren, or to fall themselves by their Hands.—He has excited domestic insurrections amongst us, and has endeavoured to bring on the inhabitants of our frontiers, the merciless Indian Savages, whose known rule of warfare, is an undistinguished destruction of all ages, sexes and conditions. In every stage of these Oppressions We have Petitioned for Redress in the most humble terms: Our repeated

Petitions have been answered only by repeated injury. A Prince, whose character is thus marked by every act which may define a Tyrant, is unfit to be the ruler of a free people. Nor have We been wanting in attentions to our British brethren. We have warned them from time to time of attempts by their legislature to extend an unwarrantable jurisdiction over us. We have reminded them of the circumstances of our emigration and settlement here. We have appealed to their native justice and magnanimity, and we have conjured them by the ties of our common kindred to disavow these usurpations, which would inevitably interrupt our connections and correspondence. They too have been deaf to the voice of justice and of consanguinity. We must, therefore, acquiesce in the necessity, which denounces our Separation, and hold them, as we hold the rest of mankind, Enemies in War, in Peace Friends.

WE, THEREFORE, the Representatives of the UNITED STATES OF AMERICA, in General Congress Assembled, appealing to the Supreme Judge of the world for the rectitude of our intentions, do, in the Name and by Authority of the good People of these Colonies, solemnly publish and declare, That these United Colonies are, and of Right ought to be FREE AND IN-DEPENDENT STATES; that they are Absolved from all Allegiance to the British Crown, and that all political connection between them and the State of Great Britain, is and ought to be totally dissolved; and that as Free and Independent States, they have full Power to levy War, conclude Peace, contract Alliances, establish Commerce, and to do all other Acts and Things which Independent States may of right do.——

And for the support of this Declaration, with a firm reliance on the protection of divine Providence, we mutually pledge to each other our Lives, our Fortunes and our sacred Honor.

1776

THE AMERICAN CRISIS

THOMAS PAINE

These are the times that try men's souls: The summer soldier and the sunshine patriot will in this crisis, shrink from the service of his country; but he that stands it Now, deserves the love and thanks of man and woman. Tyranny, like hell, is not easily conquered; yet we have this consolation with us, that the harder the conflict, the more glorious the triumph. What we obtain too cheap, we esteem to[o] lightly: ——'Tis dearness only that gives everything its value. Heaven knows how to put a proper price upon its goods; and it would be strange indeed, if so celestial an article as FREEDOM should not be highly rated. Britain, with an army to enforce her tyranny, has declared that she has a right (not only to) TAX but "to BIND *us in* ALL CASES WHATSOEVER", and if being *bound in that manner,* is not slavery, then is there not such a thing as slavery upon earth. Even the expression is impious for so unlimited a power can belong only to God.

Whether the Independence of the Continent was declared too soon, or delayed too long, I will not now enter into as an argument; my own simple opinion is, that had it been eight months earlier, it would have been much better. We did not make a proper use of last winter, neither could we, while we were in a dependent state. However, the fault, if it were one, was all our own; we have none to blame but ourselves. But no great deal is lost yet; all that Howe has been doing for this month past, is rather a ravage than a conquest, which the spirit of the Jersies a year ago would have quickly repulsed, and which time and a little resolution will soon recover.

I have as little superstition in me as any man living, but my secret opinion has ever been, and still is, that God Almighty will not give up a people to military destruction, or leave them unsupportedly to perish, who have so earnestly and so repeatedly sought to avoid the calamities of war, by every decent method which wisdom could invent. Neither have I so much of the infidel in me, as to suppose that he has relinquished the government of the world, and given us up to the care of devils; and as I do not, I cannot see on what grounds the king of Britain can look up to heaven for help against us: a common murderer, a highwayman, or a house-breaker, has as good a pretence as he.

'Tis surprising to see how rapidly a panic will sometimes run through a country. All nations and ages have been subject to them: Britain has trembled like an ague at the report of a French fleet of flat-bottomed boats; and in the fourteenth century the whole English army, after ravaging the kingdom of France, was driven back like men petrified with fear; and this brave exploit was performed by a few broken forces collected and headed by a woman, Joan of Arc. Would that

heaven might inspire some Jersey maid to spirit up
her countrymen, and save her fair fellow sufferers
from ravage and ravishment! Yet panics, in some cases,
have their uses; they produce as much good as hurt.
Their duration is always short; the mind soon grows
through them, and acquires a firmer habit than before.
But their peculiar advantage is, that they are the
touchstones of sincerity and hypocrisy, and bring
things and men to light, which might otherwise have
lain forever undiscovered. In fact, they have the same
effect on secret traitors which an imaginary apparition
would have upon a private murderer. They sift out the
hidden thoughts of man, and hold them up in public
to the world. Many a disguised tory has lately shown
his head, that shall penitentially solemnize with curses
the day on which Howe arrived upon the Delaware.

As I was with the troops at Fort-Lee, and marched
with them to the edge of Pennsylvania, I am well ac-
quainted with many circumstances, which those who
live at a distance, know but little or nothing of. Our
situation there was exceedingly cramped, the place
being a narrow neck of land between the North-River
and the Hackensack. Our force was inconsiderable,
being not one-fourth so great as Howe could bring
against us. We had no army at hand to have relieved
the garrison, had we shut ourselves up and stood on
our defence. Our ammunition, light artillery, and the
best part of our stores, had been removed, on the apprehension that Howe would endeavor to penetrate
the Jerseys, in which case Fort-Lee could be of no use
to us; for it must occur to every thinking man, whether
in the army or not, that these kind of field forts are

only for temporary purposes, and last in use no longer
than the enemy directs his force against the particular
object, which such forts are raised to defend. Such was
our situation and condition at Fort-Lee on the morning of the 20th of November, when an officer arrived
with information that the enemy with 200 boats had
landed about seven miles above: Major General Green,
who commanded the garrison, immediately ordered
them under arms, and sent express to General Washington at the town of Hackensack, distant by the way
of the ferry, six miles. Our first object was to secure
the bridge over the Hackensack, which laid up the
river between the enemy and us, about six miles from
us, and three from them. General Washington arrived
in about three-quarters of an hour, and marched at
the head of the troops towards the bridge, which place
I expected we should have a brush for; however, they
did not choose to dispute it with us, and the greatest
part of our troops went over the bridge, the rest over
the ferry, except some which passed at a mill on a small
creek, between the bridge and the ferry, and made
their way through some marshy grounds up to the
town of Hackensack, and there passed the river. We
brought off as much baggage as the wagons could con-
tain, the rest was lost. The simple object was to bring
off the garrison, and march them on till they could be
strengthened by the Jersey or Pennsylvania militia, so
as to be enabled to make a stand. We staid four days
at Newark, collected our out-posts with some of the
Jersey militia, and marched out twice to meet the
enemy, on being informed that they were advancing,
though our numbers were greatly inferior to theirs.

Howe, in my little opinion, committed a great error in generalship in not throwing a body of forces off from Staten-Island through Amboy, by which means he might have seized all our stores at Brunswick, and intercepted our march into Pennsylvania but if we believe the power of hell to be limited, we must likewise believe that their agents are under some providential control.

I shall not now attempt to give all the particulars of our retreat to the Delaware; suffice it for the present to say, that both officers and men, though greatly harassed and fatigued, frequently without rest, covering, or provision, the inevitable consequences of a long retreat, bore it with a manly and martial spirit. All their wishes centered in one, which was, that the country would turn out and help them to drive the enemy back. *Voltaire* has remarked that King William never appeared to full advantage but in difficulties and in action; the same remark may be made on General Washington, for the character fits him. There is a natural firmness in some minds which cannot be unlocked by trifles, but which, when unlocked, discovers a cabinet of fortitude; and I reckon it among those kind of public blessings, which we do not immediately see, that God hath blessed him with uninterrupted health, and given him a mind that can even flourish upon care.

I shall conclude this paper with some miscellaneous remarks on the state of our affairs; and shall begin with asking the following question, Why is it that the enemy have left the New-England provinces, and made these middle ones the seat of war? The answer is easy: New

England is not infested with tories, and we are. I have been tender in raising the cry against these men, and used numberless arguments to show them their danger, but it will not do to sacrifice a world either to their folly or their baseness. The period is now arrived, in which either they or we must change our sentiments, or one or both must fall. And what is a tory? Good God! what is he? I should not be afraid to go with a hundred Whigs against a thousand tories, were they to attempt to get into arms. Every tory is a coward; for servile, slavish, self-interested fear is the foundation of toryism; and a man under such influence, though he may be cruel, never can be brave.

But, before the line of irrecoverable separation be drawn between us, let us reason the matter together: Your conduct is an invitation to the enemy, yet not one in a thousand of you has heart enough to join him. Howe is as much deceived by you as the American cause is injured by you. He expects you will all take up arms, and flock to his standard, with muskets on your shoulders. Your opinions are of no use to him, unless you support him personally, for 'tis soldiers, and not torries, that he wants.

I once felt all that kind of anger, which a man ought to feel, against the mean principles that are held by the tories: A noted one, who kept a tavern at Amboy, was standing at his door, with as pretty a child in his hand, about eight or nine years old, as I ever saw, and after speaking his mind as freely as he thought was prudent, finished with this unfatherly expression, *"Well! give me peace in my day."* Not a man lives on the continent but fully believes that a separation must some time or other finally take place, and a generous parent should have said, *"If there must be trouble, let it be in my day, that my child may have peace";* and this single reflection, well applied, is sufficient to awaken every man to duty. Not a place upon earth might be so happy as America. Her situation is remote from all the wrangling world, and she has nothing to do but to trade with them. A man can distinguish himself between temper and principle, and I am as confident, as I am that God governs the world, that America will never be happy till she gets clear of foreign dominion. Wars, without ceasing, will break out till that period arrives, and the continent must in the end be conqueror; for though the flame of liberty may sometimes cease to shine, the coal can never expire.

America did not, nor does not want force; but she wanted a proper application of that force. Wisdom is not the purchase of a day, and it is no wonder that we should err at the first setting off. From an excess of tenderness, we were unwilling to raise an army, and trusted our cause to the temporary defence of a well-meaning militia. A summer's experience has now taught us better; yet with those troops, while they were collected, we were able to set bounds to the progress of the enemy, and, thank God! they are again assembling. I always considered militia as the best troops in the world for a sudden exertion, but they will not do for a long campaign. Howe, it is probable, will make an attempt on this city; should he fail on this side the Delaware, he is ruined. If he succeeds, our cause is not ruined. He stakes all on his side against a part on ours; admitting he succeeds, the consequence will be, that armies from both ends of the continent will march to assist their suffering friends in the middle states; for he cannot go everywhere, it is impossible. I consider Howe as the greatest enemy the tories have; he is bringing a war into their country, which, had it not been for him and partly for themselves, they had been clear of. Should he now be expelled, I wish with all the devotion of a Christian, that the names of whig and tory may never more be mentioned; but should the tories give him encouragement to come, or assistance if he come, I as sincerely wish that our next year's arms may expel them from the continent, and the Congress appropriate their possessions to the relief of those who have suffered in well-doing. A single successful battle next year will settle the whole. America could carry on a two years' war by the confiscation of the property of disaffected persons, and be made happy by their expulsion. Say not that this is revenge, call it rather the soft resentment of a suffering people, who, having no object in view but the GOOD of ALL, have staked their OWN ALL upon a seemingly doubtful event. Yet it is folly to argue against determined hardness; eloquence may strike the ear, and the language of sorrow draw forth the tear of compassion, but nothing can reach the heart that is steeled with prejudice.

Quitting this class of men, I turn with the warm ardor of a friend to those who have nobly stood, and are yet determined to stand the matter out: I call not upon a few, but upon all: not on THIS state or THAT state, but on EVERY state: up and help us; lay your shoulders to the wheel; better have too much force than too little, when so great an object is at stake. Let it be told to the future world, that in the depth of winter, when nothing but hope and virtue could survive, that the city and the country, alarmed at one common danger, came forth to meet and to repulse it. Say not that thousands are gone, turn out your tens of thousands; throw not the burden of the day upon Providence, but *"show your faith by your works,"* that God may bless you. It matters not where you live, or what rank of life you hold, the evil or the blessing will reach you all. The far and the near, the home counties and the back, the rich and the poor, will suffer or rejoice alike. The heart that feels not now is dead; the blood of his children will curse his cowardice, who shrinks back at a time when a little might have saved the whole, and made *them* happy. I love the man that can smile in trouble, that can gather strength from distress, and grow brave by reflection. 'Tis the business of little minds to shrink; but he whose heart is firm, and whose conscience approves his conduct, will pursue his principles unto death. My own line of reasoning is to myself as straight and clear as a ray of light. Not all the treasures of the world, so far as I believe, could have induced me to support an offensive war, for I think it murder; but if a thief breaks into my house, burns and destroys my property, and kills or threatens to kill me, or those that are in it, and to *"bind me in all cases whatsoever"* to his absolute will, am I to suffer it? What signifies it to me, whether he who does it is a king or a common man; my countryman or not my countryman; whether it be done by an individual villain, or an army of them? If we reason to the root of things we shall find no difference; neither can any just

cause be assigned why we should punish in the one
case and pardon in the other. Let them call me rebel,
and welcome, I feel no concern from it; but I should
suffer the misery of devils, were I to make a whore of
my soul by swearing allegiance to one whose character
is that of a sottish, stupid, stubborn, worthless, brutish
man. I conceive likewise a horrid idea in receiving
mercy from a being, who at the last day shall be shriek-
ing to the rocks and mountains to cover him, and fleeing with terror from the orphan, the widow, and the
slain of America.

There are cases which cannot be overdone by language, and this is one. There are persons, too, who see
not the full extent of the evil which threatens them;
they solace themselves with hopes that the enemy, if he
succeed, will be merciful. It is the madness of folly, to
expect mercy from those who have refused to do
justice; and even mercy, where conquest is the object,
is only a trick of war; The cunning of the fox is as
murderous as the violence of the wolf, and we ought
to guard equally against both. Howe's first object is,
partly by threats and partly by promises, to terrify or
seduce the people to deliver up their arms and receive
mercy. The ministry recommended the same plan to
Gage, and this is what the tories call making their
peace, *"a peace which passeth all understanding"*
indeed! A peace which would be the immediate fore-
runner of a worse ruin than any we have yet thought
of. Ye men of Pennsylvania, do reason upon these
things! Were the back counties to give up their arms,
they would fall an easy prey to the Indians, who are all
armed: this perhaps is what some tories would not be

sorry for. Were the home counties to deliver up their arms, they would be exposed to the resentment of the back counties, who would then have it in their power to chastise their defection at pleasure. And were any one state to give up its arms, THAT state must be garrisoned by all Howe's army of Britons and Hessians to preserve it from the anger of the rest. Mutual fear is the principal link in the chain of mutual love, and woe be to that state that breaks the compact. Howe is mercifully inviting you to barbarous destruction, and men must be either rogues or fools that will not see it. I dwell not upon the vapors of imagination; I bring reason to your ears, and, in language as plain as A, B, C, hold up truth to your eyes.

I thank *God* that I fear not. I see no real cause for fear. I know our situation well, and can see the way out of it. While our army was collected, Howe dared not risk a battle; and it is no credit to him that he decamped from the White Plains, and waited a mean opportunity to ravage the defenseless Jerseys; but it is great credit to us, that, with a handful of men, we sustained an orderly retreat for near an hundred miles, brought off our ammunition, all our fieldpieces, the greatest part of our stores, and had four rivers to pass. None can say that our retreat was precipitate, for we were near three weeks in performing it, that the country might have time to come in. Twice we marched back to meet the enemy, and remained out till dark. The sign of fear was not seen in our camp, and had not some of the cowardly and disaffected inhabitants spread false alarms through the country, the Jersies had never been ravaged. Once more we are again

collected and collecting, our new army at both ends of
the continent is recruiting fast, and we shall be able
to open the next campaign with sixty thousand men,
well-armed and clothed. This is our situation, and who
will may know it. By perseverance and fortitude we
have the prospect of a glorious issue; by cowardice and
submission, the sad choice of a variety of evils—a
ravaged country—a depopulated city—habitations without safety, and slavery without hope—our homes turned
into barracks and bawdy-houses for Hessians, and a
future race to provide for, whose fathers we shall doubt
of. Look on this picture and weep over it! and if there
yet remains one thoughtless wretch who believes it not,
let him suffer it unlamented.

1776

THE LIBERTY SONG

JOHN DICKINSON

Come join hand in hand, brave Americans all,
And rouse your bold hearts at fair Liberty's call;
No tyrannous acts, shall suppress your just claim,
Nor stain with dishonor America's name.
   In freedom we're born, and in freedom
      we'll live;
   Our purses are ready,
   Steady, Friends, steady,
   Not as *slaves,* but as *freemen* our money
      we'll give.

Our worthy forefathers—let's give them a cheer—
To climates unknown did courageously steer;
Thro' oceans to deserts, for freedom they came,
And, dying, bequeath'd us their freedom and fame.

Their generous bosoms all dangers despis'd,
So highly, so wisely, their birthrights they priz'd;
We'll keep what they gave, we will piously keep,
Nor frustrate their toils on the land or the deep.

The Tree, their own hands had to Liberty rear'd,
They lived to behold growing strong and rever'd;

With transport then cried,—"Now our wishes we gain,
For our children shall gather the fruits of our pain."

How sweet are the labors that freemen endure,
That they shall enjoy all the profit, secure,—
No more such sweet labors Americans know,
If Britons shall reap what Americans sow.

Swarms of placemen and pensioners soon will appear,
Like locusts deforming the charms of the year:
Suns vainly will rise, showers vainly descend,
If we are to drudge for what others shall spend.

Then join hand in hand, brave Americans all,
By uniting we stand, by dividing we fall;
In so righteous a cause let us hope to succeed,
For Heaven approves of each generous deed.

All ages shall speak with amaze and applause,
Of the courage we'll show in support of our laws;
To die we can bear,—but to serve we disdain,
For shame is to freemen more dreadful than pain.

This bumper I crown for our sovereign's health,
And this for Britannia's glory and wealth;
That wealth, and that glory immortal may be,
If she is but just, and we are but free.
   In freedom we're born, *etc.*

1768

SUPPOSED SPEECH
OF JOHN ADAMS

DANIEL WEBSTER

Sink or swim, live or die, survive or perish, I give my hand and my heart to this vote. It is true, indeed, that in the beginning, we aimed not at independence. But,

"There's a divinity that shapes our ends."

The injustice of England has driven us to arms; and, blinded to her own interest, she has obstinately persisted, till independence is now within our grasp. We have but to reach forth to it, and it is ours. Why then should we defer the declaration? Is any man so weak, as now to hope for a reconciliation with England, which shall leave either safety to the country and its liberties, or security to his own life and his own honor! Are not you, sir, who sit in that chair, is not he, our venerable colleague, near you, are you not both already the proscribed and predestined objects of punishment and of vengeance? Cut off from all hope of royal clemency, what are you, what can you be, while the power of England remains, but *outlaws?*

If we postpone independence, do we mean to carry

on, or to give up, the war? Do we mean to submit, and consent that we shall be ground to powder, and our country and its rights trodden down in the dust? I *know* we do not mean to submit. We NEVER *shall submit!* Do we intend to violate that most solemn obligation ever entered into by men, that plighting, before God, of our sacred honor to Washington, when putting him forth to incur the dangers of war, as well as the political hazards of the times, we promised to adhere to him in every extremity with our fortunes and our lives? I know there is not a man here, who would not rather see a general conflagration sweep over the land, or an earthquake sink it, than one jot or tittle of that plighted faith fall to the ground. For myself, having twelve months ago, in this place, moved you, that George Washington be appointed commander of the forces raised, or to be raised, for the defense of American liberty; may my right hand forget her cunning, and my tongue cleave to the roof of my mouth, if I hesitate or waver in the support I give him.

The war, then, must go on. We must fight it through. And if the war must go on, why put off the Declaration of Independence? That measure will strengthen us. It will give us character abroad. Nations will then treat with us, which they never can do while we acknowledge ourselves subjects in arms against our sovereign. Nay, I maintain that England herself will sooner treat for peace with us on the footing of independence, than consent, by repealing her acts, to acknowledge that her whole conduct toward us has been a course of injustice and oppression. Her pride will be less wounded by

submitting to that course of things, which now pre-
destinates our independence, than by yielding the
points in controversy to her rebellious subjects. The
former, she would regard as the result of fortune; the
latter, she would feel as her own deep disgrace. Why,
then, do we not change this from a civil to a national
war? And since we must fight it through, why not put
ourselves in a state to enjoy all the benefits of victory,
if we gain the victory.

If we fail, it can be no worse for us. But we shall
not fail. The cause will raise up armies; the cause will
create navies. The people—the people, if we are true to
them, will carry us, and will carry themselves, glori-
ously through this struggle. I care not how fickle other
people have been found. I know the people of these
colonies; and I know that resistance to British aggression is deep and settled in their hearts, and can not be
eradicated. Sir, the Declaration of Independence will
inspire the people with increased courage. Instead of
a long and bloody war for the restoration of privileges,
for redress of grievances, for chartered immunities,
held under a British king, set before them the glorious
object of entire independence, and it will breathe into
them anew the spirit of life.

Read this declaration at the head of the army; every
sword will be drawn, and the solemn vow uttered to
maintain it or perish on the bed of honor. Publish it
from the pulpit; religion will approve it, and the love
of religious liberty will cling around it, resolved to
stand with it or fall with it. Send it to the public halls;
proclaim it there; let *them* see it, who saw their

brothers and their sons fall on the field of Bunker Hill, and in the streets of Lexington and Concord, and the very walls will cry out in its support.

Sir, I know the uncertainty of human affairs, but I see—I see clearly through this day's business. You and I, indeed, may rue it. We may not live to see the time this declaration shall be made good. We may die; die colonists; die slaves; die, it may be, ignominiously, and on the scaffold. Be it so: be it so. If it be the pleasure of Heaven that my country shall require the poor offering of my life, the victim shall be ready at the appointed hour of sacrifice, come when that hour may. But while I do live, let me have a country, or at least the *hope* of a country, and that a FREE *country*.

But whatever may be our fate, be assured—be assured that this declaration will stand. It may cost treasure, and it may cost blood; but it will stand, and it will richly compensate for both. Through the thick gloom of the present I see the brightness of the future as the sun in heaven. We shall make this a glorious, an immortal day. When we are in our graves, our children will honor it. They will celebrate it with thanksgiving, with festivity, with bonfires, and illuminations. On its annual return they will shed tears,—copious, gushing tears; not of subjection and slavery, not of agony and distress, but of exultation, of gratitude, and of joy.

Sir, before God, I believe the hour is come. My judgment approves the measure, and my whole heart is in it. All that I have, and all that I am, and all that I hope in this life, I am now ready here to stake upon it; and I leave off as I began, that, live or die, survive or

perish, I am for the declaration. It is my living sentiment, and, by the blessing of God, it shall be my dying
sentiment; independence *now,* and INDEPENDENCE FOR-
EVER.

1826

PRESIDENT ROOSEVELT'S WAR MESSAGE

Mr. Vice President, Mr. Speaker, members of the Senate and the House of Representatives:

Yesterday, Dec. 7, 1941—a date which will live in infamy—the United States of America was suddenly and deliberately attacked by naval and air forces of the empire of Japan.

The United States was at peace with that nation, and, at the solicitation of Japan, was still in conversation with its government and its Emperor looking toward the maintenance of peace in the Pacific.

Indeed, one hour after Japanese air squadrons had commenced bombing in the American island of Oahu the Japanese Ambassador to the United States and his colleague delivered to our Secretary of State a formal reply to a recent American message. And, while this reply stated that it seemed useless to continue the existing diplomatic negotiations, it contained no threat or hint of war or of armed attack.

It will be recorded that the distance of Hawaii from Japan makes it obvious that the attack was deliberately planned many days or even weeks ago. During the intervening time the Japanese Government has deliberately sought to deceive the United States by false statements and expressions of hope for continued peace.

The attack yesterday on the Hawaiian Islands has caused severe damage to American naval and military forces. I regret to tell you that very many American lives have been lost. In addition, American ships have been reported torpedoed on the high seas between San Francisco and Honolulu.

Yesterday the Japanese Government also launched an attack against Malaya.

Last night Japanese forces attacked Hong Kong.

Last night Japanese forces attacked Guam.

Last night Japanese forces attacked the Philippine Islands.

Last night the Japanese attacked Wake Island.

And this morning the Japanese attacked Midway Island.

Japan has therefore undertaken a surprise offensive extending throughout the Pacific area. The facts of yesterday and today speak for themselves. The people of the United States have already formed their opinions and well understand the implications to the very life and safety of our nation.

As Commander in Chief of the Army and Navy I have directed that all measures be taken for our defense, that always will our whole nation remember the character of the onslaught against us.

No matter how long it may take us to overcome this premeditated invasion, the American people, in their righteous might, will win through to absolute victory.

I believe that I interpret the will of the Congress and of the people when I assert that we will not only defend ourselves to the uttermost but will make it very certain that this form of treachery shall never again endanger us.

Hostilities exist. There is no blinking at the fact that our people, our territory and our interests are in grave danger.

With confidence in our armed forces, with the unbounded determination of our people, we will gain the inevitable triumph. So help us God.

I ask that the Congress declare that since the unprovoked and dastardly attack by Japan on Sunday, Dec. 7, 1941, a state of war has existed between the United States and the Japanese Empire.

WAR

WILLIAM SAROYAN

Karl the Prussian is five, a splendid Teuton with a military manner of walking over the sidewalk in front of his house, and a natural discipline of speech that is both admirable and refreshing, as if the child understood the essential dignity of mortal articulation and could not bear to misuse the gift, opening his mouth only rarely and then only to utter a phrase of no more than three or four words, wholly to the point and amazingly pertinent. He lives in a house across the street and is the pride of his grandfather, an erect man of fifty with a good German moustache whose picture appeared in a newspaper several years ago in connection with a political campaign. This man began teaching Karl to walk as soon as the boy was able to stand on his legs, and he could be seen with the small blond boy in blue overalls, moving up and down a half block of sidewalk, holding the child's hands and showing him how to step forward precisely and a bit pompously, in the German royalist manner, knees stiff, each step resembling an arrested kick.

Every morning for several months the old man and the little boy practised walking, and it was a very pleasant routine to watch. Karl's progress was rapid but hardly hurried, and he seemed to understand the quiet sternness of his grandfather, and even from across the street it was easy to see that he believed in the importance of being able to walk in a dignified manner, and wished to learn to do it the way his grandfather was teaching him to do it. Fundamentally, the little boy and the old man were the same, the only difference being the inevitable difference of age and experience, and Karl showed no signs of wishing to rebel against the discipline imposed upon him by the old man.

After a while the little boy was walking up and down the stretch of sidewalk in front of his house, unassisted by the old man, who watched him quietly from the steps of his house, smoking a pipe and looking upon the boy with an expression of severity which was at the same time an expression of pride, and the little boy kicked himself forward very nicely. The walk was certainly old-fashioned and certainly a little undemocratic, but everyone in this neighborhood liked Karl and regarded him as a very fine little man. There was something about a small boy walking that way that was satisfying. True Teutons appreciate the importance of such relatively automatic functions as breathing, walking and talking, and they are able to bother about these simple actions in a manner that is both reasonable and dignified. To them, apparently, breathing and walking and talking are related closely to living in general, and the fuss they make about these actions isn't therefore the least ridiculous.

People living in the houses of this block have been breeding well during the past six or seven years, and

the street has a fair population of children, all of them
healthy and interesting, to me extremely interesting.
Karl is only one of the group, and he is mentioned
first because he is perhaps the only one who has been
taught a conscious racial technique of living. The
other children belong to a number of races, and while
the basic traits of each race are apparent in each child,
these traits have not been emphasized and strengthened as they have been emphasized and strengthened
in Karl. In other words, each child is of his race naturally and instinctively, and it is likely that except for
the instruction of his grandfather, Karl himself would
now be more like the other children, more artless and
unrepressed. He would not have the military manner
of walking which is the chief difference between him
and the other children, and the mannerism which
sometimes gets on the nerves of Josef, the Slovenian
boy who lives in the flat downstairs.

Josef is almost a year older than Karl, and he is a
lively boy whose every action suggests inward laughter.
He has the bright and impish face of his father who
is by trade a baker, and he is the sort of boy who talks
a lot, who is interested in everything and everyone
around him, and who is always asking questions. He
wants to know the names of people, and his favorite
question is *where have you been?* He asks this question in a way that suggests he is hoping you have just
returned from some very strange and wonderful place,
not like anything he has ever seen, and perhaps not
like any place on earth, and I myself have always been
embarrassed because I have had to tell him that I have
come from a place no more wonderful than town,

which he himself has seen at least a half dozen times.

Karl hardly ever runs, while Josef hardly ever walks, and is almost always running or skipping or leaping, as if *going* from one place to another was a good deal more important to him than leaving one place and reaching another place, as if, I mean, the mere going was what pleased him, rather than any specific object in going. Josef plays, while Karl performs. The Slav is himself first and his race afterwards, while the Teuton is his race first and himself afterwards. I have been studying the children who live in this block for a number of years, and I hope no one will imagine that I am making up things about them in order to be able to write a little story, for I am not making up anything. The little episode of yesterday evening would be trivial and pointless if I had not watched the growth of these boys, and I only regret that I do not know more about Irving, the Jewish boy who cried so bitterly while Karl and Josef struck each other.

Irving came with his mother and father to this block last November, not quite four months ago, but I did not begin to see much of him until a month later when he began to appear in the street. He is a melancholy-looking boy, about Josef's age, and of the sort described generally as introspective, seeming to feel safer within himself. I suppose his parents are having him educated musically, for he has the appearance of someone who ought to develop into a pretty fine violinist or pianist, the large serious head, the slight body, and a delicate nervous system.

One evening, on the way to the grocer's, I saw Irving sitting on the steps of his house, apparently dreaming the unspeakably beautiful dream of a child bewildered by the strangeness of being, and I hoped to speak to him quietly and try to find out, if possible, what was going on in his mind, but when he saw me coming toward him, he got up swiftly and scrambled up the steps and into the house, looking startled and very much afraid. I would give my phonograph to know what Irving had been dreaming that evening, for I believe it would somehow make explicable his weeping last night.

Karl is solid and very sure of his stance, extremely certain of himself because of the fact that discipline prohibits undue speculation regarding circumstances unrelated to himself, while Josef, on the other hand, though no less certain of himself, is a good deal less solid because of the fact that a lively curiosity about all things impels him to keep in motion, and to do things without thinking. The presence of Irving on this street is solid enough, but there is something about his presence that is both amusing and saddening, as if he himself cannot figure it out and as if, for all he knows, he were somewhere else. Irving is not at all certain of himself. He is neither disciplined nor undisciplined, he is simply melancholy. Eventually I suppose, he will come to have the fullest understanding of himself and his relation to all things, but at the moment he is much too bewildered to have any definite viewpoint on the matter.

Not long ago there were riots in Paris, and shortly afterwards a civil war developed in Austria. It is a well-known fact that Russia is preparing to defend herself against Japan, and everyone is aware of the fidgetiness which has come over all of Europe because of the nationalistic program of the present dictator of Germany.

I mention these facts because they have a bearing on the story I am telling. As Joyce would say, the earth haveth childers everywhere, and the little episode of last night is to me as significant as the larger episodes in Europe must be to the men who have grown up and become no longer children. At least, seemingly.

The day began yesterday with thick fog, followed by a brief shower. By three in the afternoon the sun was shining and the sky was clear except for a number of white clouds, the kind of clouds that indicate good weather, a clear moment, clean air, and so on. The weather changes this way in San Francisco. In the morning the weather is apt to be winter weather, and in the afternoon the winter weather is apt to change suddenly to spring weather, any season of the year. Hardly anyone is aware of seasons out here. We have all seasons all the year round.

When I left my room in the morning, none of the children of this street was outdoors, but when I returned in the evening, I saw Josef and Irving standing together on my side of the street, in front of Irving's house, talking. Karl was across the street, in front of his house, walking in the military manner I have described, looking pompous in an amusing sort of way and seeming to be very proud of himself. Farther down the street were five little girls, playing a hopping game on the sidewalk: Josef's big sister, two Irish girls who were sisters, and two Italian girls who were sisters.

After rain the air clears up and it is very pleasant to

be abroad, and these children were playing in the
street, in the sunlight. It was a very fine moment to be
alive and to have love for all others alive in one's time,
and I mention this to show that the occasional ugliness
of the human heart is not necessarily the consequence
of some similar ugliness in nature. And we know that
when the European countryside was loveliest this had
no effect on the progress of the last war, and that the
rate of killing remained just as high as it had been
during the bad weather, and that the only thing that
happened as a consequence of the lovely weather was
some touching poetry by young soldiers who wanted to
create, who wanted wives and homes, and who did not
want to be killed.

Walking past Josef and Irving, I heard Josef say,
speaking of Karl: Look at him. Look at the way he's
walking. Why does he walk that way?

I had known for some time that Josef resented the
pompous certainty of Karl's manner of walking, and
therefore his remarks did not surprise me. Besides, I
have already said that he was naturally curious about
all things that came within the range of his consciousness, and that he was always asking questions. It
seemed to me that his interest in Karl's way of walking
was largely aesthetic, and I didn't seem to detect any
malice in his speech. I did not hear Irving make a
reply, and I came directly to my room. I had a letter
to write and I went to work on it, and when it was
finished I stood at the window of my room, studying
the street. The small girls had disappeared, but Karl
was still across the street, and Josef and Irving were

still together. It was beginning to be dusk, and the
street was very quiet.

I do not know how it happened, but when Josef
and Irving began crossing the street, going to Karl, I
saw a whole nation moving the line of its army to the
borders of another nation, and the little boys seemed
so very innocent and likable, and whole nations
seemed so much like the little boys that I could not
avoid laughing to myself. Oh, I thought, there will
probably be another war before long, and the children will make a great fuss in the world, but it will
probably be very much like what is going to happen
now. For I was certain that Josef and Karl were going
to express their hatred for each other, the hatred that
was stupid and wasteful and the result of ignorance
and immaturity, by striking one another, as whole
nations, through stupid hatred, seek to dominate or
destroy one another.

It happened across the street, two small boys striking
each other, a third small boy crying about it, whole
nations at war on the earth. I did not hear what Josef
said to Karl, or what Karl said to Josef, and I am not
sure just how the fight started, but I have an idea that
it started a long while before the two boys began to
strike each other, a year ago perhaps, perhaps a century
ago. I saw Josef touch Karl, each of them fine little boys,
and I saw Karl shove Josef, and I saw the little Jewish
boy watching them, horrified and silent, almost
stunned. When the little Teuton and the little Slav
began to strike each other in earnest, the little Jew
began to weep. It was lovely—not the striking, but the

weeping of the little Jew. The whole affair lasted only a moment or two, but the implication was whole, and the most enduring and refreshing part of it is this weeping I heard. Why did he cry? He was not involved. He was only a witness, as I was a witness. Why did he cry?

I wish I knew more about the little Jewish boy. I can only imagine that he cried because the existence of hatred and ugliness in the heart of man is a truth, and this is as far as I can go with the theory.

PART TWO

MEN IN ACTION

From THE RED BADGE
OF COURAGE

STEPHEN CRANE

When another night came the columns, changed
to purple streaks, filed across two pontoon bridges. A
glaring fire wine-tinted the waters of the river. Its rays,
shining upon the moving masses of troops, brought
forth here and there sudden gleams of silver or gold.
Upon the other shore a dark and mysterious range of
hills was curved against the sky. The insect voices of
the night sang solemnly.

After this crossing the youth assured himself that
at any moment they might be suddenly and fearfully
assaulted from the caves of the lowering woods. He
kept his eyes watchfully upon the darkness.

But his regiment went unmolested to a camping
place, and its soldiers slept the brave sleep of wearied
men. In the morning they were routed out with early
energy, and hustled along a narrow road that led deep
into the forest.

It was during this rapid march that the regiment
lost many of the marks of a new command.

The men had begun to count the miles upon their
fingers, and they grew tired. "Sore feet an' damned
short rations, that's all," said the loud soldier. There
was perspiration and grumblings. After a time they

began to shed their knapsacks. Some tossed them unconcernedly down; others hid them carefully, asserting their plans to return for them at some convenient time. Men extricated themselves from thick shirts. Presently few carried anything but their necessary clothing, blankets, haversacks, canteens, and arms and ammunition. "You can now eat and shoot," said the tall soldier to the youth. "That's all you want to do."

There was sudden change from the ponderous infantry of theory to the light and speedy infantry of practice. The regiment, relieved of a burden, received a new impetus. But there was much loss of valuable knapsacks, and, on the whole, very good shirts.

But the regiment was not yet veteran-like in appearance. Veteran regiments in the army were likely to be very small aggregations of men. Once, when the command had first come to the field, some perambulating veterans, noting the length of their column, had accosted them thus: "Hey, fellers, what brigade is that?" And when the men had replied that they formed a regiment and not a brigade, the older soldiers had laughed, and said, "O Gawd!"

Also, there was too great a similarity in the hats. The hats of a regiment should properly represent the history of headgear for a period of years. And, moreover, there were no letters of faded gold speaking from the colors. They were new and beautiful, and the color-bearer habitually oiled the pole.

Presently the army again sat down to think. The odor of the peaceful pines was in the men's nostrils. The sounds of monotonous axe blows rang through the forest, and the insects, nodding upon their perches, crooned like old women. The youth returned to his theory of a blue demonstration.

One gray dawn, however, he was kicked in the leg by the tall soldier, and then, before he was entirely awake, he found himself running down a wood road in the midst of men who were panting from the first effects of speed. His canteen banged rhythmically upon his thigh, and his haversack bobbed softly.

His musket bounced a trifle from his shoulder at each stride and made his cap feel uncertain upon his head.

He could hear the men whisper jerky sentences: "Say—what's all this—about?" "What th' thunder—we —skedaddlin' this way fer?" "Billie—keep off m' feet. Yeh run—like a cow." And the loud soldier's shrill voice could be heard: "What th' devil they in sich a hurry for?"

The youth thought the damp fog of early morning moved from the rush of a great body of troops. From the distance came a sudden spatter of firing.

He was bewildered. As he ran with his comrades he strenuously tried to think, but all he knew was that if he fell down those coming behind would tread upon him. All his faculties seemed to be needed to guide him over and past obstructions. He felt carried along by a mob.

The sun spread disclosing rays, and, one by one, regiments burst into view like armed men just born of the earth. The youth perceived that the time had come. He was about to be measured. For a moment he felt in the face of his great trial like a babe, and the flesh over his heart seemed very thin. He seized time to look about him calculatingly.

But he instantly saw that it would be impossible for him to escape from the regiment. It inclosed him. And there were iron laws of tradition and law on four sides. He was in a moving box.

As he perceived this fact it occurred to him that he had never wished to come to the war. He had not enlisted of his free will. He had been dragged by the merciless government. And now they were taking him out to be slaughtered.

The regiment slid down a bank and wallowed across a little stream. The mournful current moved slowly on, and from the water, shaded black, some white bubble eyes looked at the men.

As they climbed the hill on the farther side artillery began to boom. Here the youth forgot many things as he felt a sudden impulse of curiosity. He scrambled up the bank with a speed that could not be exceeded by a bloodthirsty man.

He expected a battle scene.

There were some little fields girted and squeezed by a forest. Spread over the grass and in among the tree trunks, he could see knots and waving lines of skirmishers who were running hither and thither and firing at the landscape. A dark battle line lay upon a sun-struck clearing that gleamed orange color. A flag fluttered.

Other regiments floundered up the bank. The brigade was formed in line of battle, and after a pause started slowly through the woods in the rear of the receding skirmishers, who were continually melting

into the scene to appear again farther on. They were
always busy as bees, deeply absorbed in their little
combats.

The youth tried to observe everything. He did not
use care to avoid trees and branches, and his forgotten
feet were constantly knocking against stones or getting
entangled in briers. He was aware that these battalions
with their commotions were woven red and startling
into the gentle fabric of softened greens and browns.
It looked to be a wrong place for a battlefield.

The skirmishers in advance fascinated him. Their
shots into thickets and at distant and prominent trees
spoke to him of tragedies—hidden, mysterious, solemn.

Once the line encountered the body of a dead soldier. He lay upon his back staring at the sky. He was
dressed in an awkward suit of yellowish brown. The
youth could see that the soles of his shoes had been
worn to the thinness of writing paper, and from a
great rent in one the dead foot projected piteously.
And it was as if fate had betrayed the soldier. In death
it exposed to his enemies that poverty which in life
he had perhaps concealed from his friends.

The ranks opened covertly to avoid the corpse. The
invulnerable dead man forced a way for himself. The
youth looked keenly at the ashen face. The wind raised
the tawny beard. It moved as if a hand were stroking
it. He vaguely desired to walk around and around the
body and stare; the impulse of the living to try to read
in dead eyes the answer to the Question.

During the march the ardor which the youth had
acquired when out of view of the field rapidly faded
to nothing. His curiosity was quite easily satisfied. If

an intense scene had caught him with its wild swing as he came to the top of the bank, he might have gone roaring on. This advance upon Nature was too calm. He had opportunity to reflect. He had time in which to wonder about himself and to attempt to probe his sensations.

Absurd ideas took hold upon him. He thought that he did not relish the landscape. It threatened him. A coldness swept over his back, and it is true that his trousers felt to him that they were no fit for his legs at all.

A house standing placidly in distant fields had to him an ominous look. The shadows of the woods were formidable. He was certain that in this vista there lurked fierce-eyed hosts. The swift thought came to him that the generals did not know what they were about. It was all a trap. Suddenly those close forests would bristle with rifle barrels. Iron-like brigades would appear in the rear. They were all going to be sacrificed. The generals were stupids. The enemy would presently swallow the whole command. He glared about him, expecting to see the stealthy approach of his death.

He thought that he must break from the ranks and harangue his comrades. They must not all be killed like pigs; and he was sure it would come to pass unless they were informed of these dangers. The generals were idiots to send them marching into a regular pen. There was but one pair of eyes in the corps. He would step forth and make a speech. Shrill and passionate words came to his lips.

The line, broken into moving fragments by the ground, went calmly on through fields and woods. The youth looked at the men nearest him, and saw, for the most part, expressions of deep interest, as if they were investigating something that had fascinated them. One or two stepped with over-valiant airs as if they were already plunged into war. Others walked as upon thin ice. The greater part of the untested men appeared quiet and absorbed. They were going to look at war, the red animal—war, the blood-swollen god. And they were deeply engrossed in this march.

As he looked the youth gripped his outcry at his throat. He saw that even if the men were tottering with fear they would laugh at his warning. They would jeer him, and, if practicable, pelt him with missiles. Admitting that he might be wrong, a frenzied declamation of the kind would turn him into a worm.

He assumed, then, the demeanor of one who knows that he is doomed alone to unwritten responsibilities. He lagged, with tragic glances at the sky. He was surprised presently by the young lieutenant of his company, who began heartily to beat him with a sword, calling out in a loud and insolent voice: "Come, young man, get up into the ranks there. No skulking'll do here." He mended his pace with suitable haste. And he hated the lieutenant, who had no appreciation of fine minds. He was a mere brute.

After a time the brigade was halted in the cathedral light of a forest. The busy skirmishers were still popping. Through the aisles of the wood could be seen the floating smoke from their rifles. Sometimes it went up in little balls, white and compact.

During this halt many men in the regiment began erecting tiny hills in front of them. They used stones,

sticks, earth, and anything they thought might turn a
bullet. Some built comparatively large ones, while
others seemed content with little ones.

This procedure caused a discussion among the men.
Some wished to fight like duellists, believing it to be
correct to stand erect and be, from their feet to their
foreheads, a mark. They said they scorned the devices
of the cautious. But the others scoffed in reply, and
pointed to the veterans on the flanks who were digging
at the ground like terriers. In a short time there was
quite a barricade along the regimental fronts. Directly
however, they were ordered to withdraw from that
place.

This astounded the youth. He forgot his stewing
over the advance movement. "Well, then, what did
they march us out here for?" he demanded of the tall
soldier. The latter with calm faith began a heavy explanation, although he had been compelled to leave a
little protection of stones and dirt to which he had devoted much care and skill.

When the regiment was aligned in another position
each man's regard for his safety caused another line of
small entrenchments. They ate their noon meal behind
a third one. They were moved from this one also. They
were marched from place to place with apparent aim-
lessness.

The youth had been taught that a man became another thing in a battle. He saw his salvation in such a
change. Hence this waiting was an ordeal to him. He
was in a fever of impatience. He considered that there
was denoted a lack of purpose on the part of the generals. He began to complain to the tall soldier. "I can't

stand this much longer," he cried. "I don't see what
good it does to make us wear out our legs for nothin'."
He wished to return to camp, knowing that this affair
was a blue demonstration; or else to go into a battle
and discover that he had been a fool in his doubts,
and was, in truth, a man of traditional courage. The
strain of present circumstances he felt to be intolerable.

The philosophical tall soldier measured a sandwich
of cracker and pork and swallowed it in a nonchalant
manner. "Oh, I suppose we must go reconnoitering
around the country jest to keep 'em from getting too
close, or to develop 'em, or something."

"Huh!" said the loud soldier.

"Well," cried the youth, still fidgeting, "I'd rather
do anything 'most than go tramping 'round the country all day doing no good to nobody and jest tiring
ourselves out."

"So would I," said the loud soldier. "It ain't right.
I tell you if anybody with any sense was a-runnin'
this army it—"

"Oh, shut up!" roared the tall private. "You little
fool. You little damn' cuss. You ain't had that there
coat and them pants on for six months, and yet you
talk as if—"

"Well, I wanta do some fighting anyway," interrupted the other. "I didn't come here to walk. I could
'ave walked to home—'round an' 'round the barn, if I
jest wanted to walk."

The tall one, red-faced, swallowed another sandwich
as if taking poison in despair.

But gradually, as he chewed, his face became again

quiet and contented. He could not rage in fierce argument in the presence of such sandwiches. During his meals he always wore an air of blissful contemplation of the food he had swallowed. His spirit seemed then to be communing with the viands.

He accepted new environment and circumstance with great coolness, eating from his haversack at every opportunity. On the march he went along with the stride of a hunter, objecting to neither gait nor distance. And he had not raised his voice when he had been ordered away from three little protective piles of earth and stone, each of which had been an engineering feat worthy of being made sacred to the name of his grandmother.

In the afternoon the regiment went out over the same ground it had taken in the morning. The landscape then ceased to threaten the youth. He had been close to it and become familiar with it.

When, however, they began to pass into a new region, his old fears of stupidity and incompetence reassailed him, but this time he doggedly let them babble. He was occupied with his problem, and in his desperation he concluded that the stupidity did not greatly matter.

Once he thought he had concluded that it would be better to get killed directly and end his troubles. Regarding death thus out of the corner of his eye, he conceived it to be nothing but rest, and he was filled with a momentary astonishment that he should have made an extraordinary commotion over the mere matter of getting killed. He would die; he would go to some place where he would be understood. It was useless to expect appreciation of his profound and fine senses from such men as the lieutenant. He must look to the grave for comprehension.

The skirmish fire increased to a long clattering sound. With it was mingled far-away cheering. A battery spoke.

Directly the youth would see the skirmishers running. They were pursued by the sound of musketry fire. After a time the hot, dangerous flashes of the rifles were visible. Smoke clouds went slowly and insolently across the fields like observant phantoms. The din became crescendo, like the roar of an oncoming train.

A brigade ahead of them and on the right went into action with a rending roar. It was as if it had exploded. And thereafter it lay stretched in the distance behind a long gray wall, that one was obliged to look twice at to make sure that it was smoke.

The youth, forgetting his neat plan of getting killed, gazed spellbound. His eyes grew wide and busy with the action of the scene. His mouth was a little ways open.

Of a sudden he felt a heavy and sad hand laid upon his shoulder. Awakening from his trance of observation he turned and beheld the loud soldier.

"It's my first and last battle, old boy," said the latter, with intense gloom. He was quite pale, and his girlish lip was trembling.

"Eh?" murmured the youth in great astonishment.

"It's my first and last battle, old boy," continued the loud soldier. "Something tells me—"

"What?"

"I'm a gone coon this first time and—and I w-want

you to take these here things—to—my—folks." He
ended in a quavering sob of pity for himself. He
handed the youth a little packet done up in a yellow
envelope.

"Why, what the devil—" began the youth again.

But the other gave him a glance as from the depths
of a tomb, and raised his limp hand in a prophetic
manner and turned away.

The brigade was halted in the fringe of a grove. The
men crouched among the trees and pointed their restless guns out at the fields. They tried to look beyond
the smoke.

Out of this haze they could see running men. Some
shouted information and gestured as they hurried.

The men of the new regiment watched and listened
eagerly, while their tongues ran on in gossip of the
battle. They mouthed rumors that had flown like birds
out of the unknown.

"They say Perry has been driven in with big loss."

"Yes, Carrott went t' th' hospital. He said he was
sick. That smart lieutenant is commanding 'G' Company. Th' boys say they won't be under Carrott no
more if they all have t' desert. They allus knew he was
a—"

"Hannises' batt'ry is took."

"It ain't either. I saw Hannises' batt'ry off on th'
left not more'n fifteen minutes ago."

"Well—"

"Th' general, he ses he is goin' t' take th' hull command of th' 304th when we go inteh action, an' then he ses we'll do sech fightin' as never another one reg'ment done."

"They say we're catchin' it over on th' left. They say th' enemy driv' our line inteh a devil of a swamp an' took Hannises' batt'ry."

"No sech thing. Hannises' batt'ry was 'long here 'bout a minute ago."

"That young Hasbrouck, he makes a good off'cer. He ain't afraid 'a nothin'."

"I met one of th' 148th Maine boys an' he ses his brigade fit th' hull rebel army fer four hours over on th' turnpike road an' killed about five thousand of 'em. He ses one more sech fight as that an' th' war'll be over."

"Bill wasn't scared either. No, sir! It wasn't that. Bill ain't a-gittin' scared easy. He was jest mad, that's what he was. When that feller trod on his hand, he up an' sed that he was willin' t' give his hand t' his country, but he be dumbed if he was goin' t' have every dumb bushwacker in th' kentry walkin' 'round on it. So he went t' th' hospital disregardless of th' fight. Three fingers was crunched. Th' dern doctor wanted t' amputate 'm, an' Bill, he raised a heluva row, I hear. He's a funny feller."

"Hear that what th' ol' colonel ses, boys? He ses he'll shoot the first man what'll turn an' run."

"He'd better try it. I'd like t' see him shoot at *me*."

"He wants t' look fer his *own* self. He don't wanta go 'round talkin' big."

"They say Perry's division's a-givin' 'em thunder."

"Ed Williams over in Company A, he ses the rebs 'll all drop their guns an' run an' holler if we onct give 'em one good lickin'."

"Oh, thunder, Ed Williams, what does he know? Ever since he got shot at on picket he's been runnin' th' war."

"Well, he—"

"Hear the news, boys? Corkright's crushed th' hull rebel right an' captured two hull divisions. We'll be back in winter quarters by a short cut t'-morrah."

"I tell yeh I've been all over that there kentry where th' rebel right is an' it's th' nastiest part th' rebel line. It's all mussed up with hills an' little damn creeks. I'll bet m' shirt Corkright never harmed 'em down there."

"Well, he's a fighter an' if they could be licked, he'd lick 'em."

The din in front swelled to a tremendous chorus. The youth and his fellows were frozen to silence. They could see a flag that tossed in the smoke angrily. Near it were the blurred and agitated forms of troops. There came a turbulent stream of men across the fields. A battery changing positions at a frantic gallop scattered the stragglers right and left.

A shell screaming like a storm banshee went over the huddled heads of the reserves. It landed in the grove, and exploding redly flung the brown earth. There was a little shower of pine needles.

Bullets began to whistle among the branches and nip at the trees. Twigs and leaves came sailing down. It was as if a thousand axes, wee and invisible, were being wielded. Many of the men were constantly dodging and ducking their heads.

The lieutenant of the youth's company was shot in the hand. He began to swear so wondrously, that a nervous laugh went along the regimental line. The officer's profanity sounded conventional. It relieved the tightened senses of the new men. It was as if he had hit his fingers with a tack hammer at home.

He held the wounded member carefully away from his side so that the blood would not drip upon his trousers.

The captain of the company, tucking his sword under his arm, produced a handkerchief and began to bind with it the lieutenant's wound. And they disputed as to how the binding should be done.

The battle flag in the distance jerked about madly. It seemed to be struggling to free itself from an agony. The billowing smoke was filled with horizontal flashes.

Men running swiftly emerged from it. They grew in numbers until it was seen that the whole command was fleeing. The flag suddenly sank down as if dying. Its motion as it fell was a gesture of despair.

Wild yells came from behind the walls of smoke. A sketch in gray and red dissolved into a moblike body of men who galloped like wild horses.

The veteran regiments on the right and left of the 304th immediately began to jeer. With the passionate song of the bullets and the banshee shrieks of shells were mingled loud catcalls and bits of facetious advice concerning places of safety.

But the new regiment was breathless with horror. "Gawd! Saunders's got crushed!" whispered the man at the youth's elbow. They shrank back and crouched as if compelled to await a flood.

The youth shot a swift glance along the blue ranks of the regiment. The profiles were motionless, carven; and afterward he remembered that the color sergeant was standing with his legs apart, as if he expected to be pushed to the ground.

The following throng went whirling around the flank. Here and there were officers carried along on the stream like exasperated chips. They were striking about them with their swords and with their left fists, punching every head they could reach. They cursed like highwaymen.

A mounted officer displayed the furious anger of a spoiled child. He raged with his head, his arms, and his legs.

Another, the commander of the brigade, was galloping about bawling. His hat was gone and his clothes were awry. He resembled a man who has come from bed to go to a fire. The hoofs of his horse often threatened the heads of the running men, but they scampered with singular fortune. In this rush they were apparently all deaf and blind. They heeded not the largest and longest of the oaths that were thrown at them from all directions.

Frequently over this tumult could be heard the grim jokes of the critical veterans; but the retreating men apparently were not even conscious of the presence of an audience.

The battle reflection that shone for an instant in the faces on the mad current made the youth feel that forceful hands from heaven would not have been able to have held him in place if he could have got intelligent control of his legs.

There was an appalling imprint upon these faces. The struggle in the smoke had pictured an exaggeration of itself on the bleached cheeks and in the eyes wild with one desire.

The sight of this stampede exerted a floodlike force that seemed able to drag sticks and stones and men from the ground. They of the reserves had to hold on. They grew pale and firm, and red and quaking.

The youth achieved one little thought in the midst of this chaos. The composite monster which had caused the other troops to flee had not then appeared. He resolved to get a view of it, and then, he thought he might very likely run better than the best of them.

There were moments of waiting. The youth thought of the village street at home before the arrival of the circus parade on a day in the spring. He remembered how he had stood, a small, thrillful boy, prepared to follow the dingy lady upon the white horse, or the band in its faded chariot. He saw the yellow road, the lines of expectant people, and the sober houses. He particularly remembered an old fellow who used to sit upon a cracker box in front of the store and feign to despise such exhibitions. A thousand details of color and form surged in his mind. The old fellow upon the cracker box appeared in middle prominence.

Some one cried, "Here they come!"

There was rustling and muttering among the men. They displayed a feverish desire to have every possible cartridge ready to their hands. The boxes were pulled around into various positions, and adjusted

with great care. It was as if seven hundred new bon-
nets were being tried on.

The tall soldier, having prepared his rifle, produced
a red handkerchief of some kind. He was engaged in
knotting it about his throat with exquisite attention
to its position, when the cry was repeated up and down
the line in a muffled roar of sound.

"Here they come! Here they come!" Gun locks
clicked.

Across the smoke-infested fields came a brown swarm
of running men who were giving shrill yells. They
came on, stooping and swinging their rifles at all angles. A flag, tilted forward, sped near the front.

As he caught sight of them the youth was momen-
tarily startled by a thought that perhaps his gun was
not loaded. He stood trying to rally his faltering intellect so that he might recollect the moment when he
had loaded, but he could not.

A hatless general pulled his dripping horse to a
stand near the colonel of the 304th. He shook his fist
in the other's face. "You've got to hold 'em back!" he
shouted savagely; "you've got to hold 'em back!"

In his agitation the colonel began to stammer. "A-all
r-right, General, all right, by Gawd! We-we'll do our
—we-we'll d-d-do—do our best, General." The general
made a passionate gesture and galloped away. The
colonel, perchance to relieve his feelings, began to scold
like a wet parrot. The youth, turning swiftly to make
sure that the rear was unmolested, saw the commander
regarding his men in a highly resentful manner, as if
he regretted above everything his association with
them.

The man at the youth's elbow was mumbling, as if to himself: "Oh, we're in for it now! oh, we're in for it now!"

The captain of the company had been pacing excitedly to and fro in the rear. He coaxed in schoolmistress fashion, as to a congregation of boys with primers. His talk was an endless repetition. "Reserve your fire, boys —don't shoot till I tell you—save your fire—wait till they get close up—don't be damned fools—"

Perspiration streamed down the youth's face, which was soiled like that of a weeping urchin. He frequently, with a nervous movement, wiped his eyes with his coat sleeve. His mouth was still a little way open.

He got the one glance at the foe-swarming field in front of him, and instantly ceased to debate the question of his piece being loaded. Before he was ready to begin—before he had announced to himself that he was about to fight—he threw the obedient, well-balanced rifle into position and fired a first wild shot. Directly he was working at his weapon like an automatic affair.

He suddenly lost concern for himself, and forgot to look at a menacing fate. He became not a man but a member. He felt that something of which he was a part —a regiment, an army, a cause, or a country—was in a crisis. He was welded into a common personality which was dominated by a single desire. For some moments he could not flee no more than a little finger can commit a revolution from a hand.

If he had thought the regiment was about to be annihilated, perhaps he could have amputated himself from it. But its noise gave him assurance. The regiment was like a firework that, once ignited, proceeds superior to circumstances until its blazing vitality fades. It wheezed and banged with a mighty power. He pictured the ground before it as strewn with the discomfited.

There was a consciousness always of the presence of his comrades about him. He felt the subtle battle brotherhood more potent even than the cause for which they were fighting. It was a mysterious fraternity born of the smoke and danger of death.

He was at a task. He was like a carpenter who has made many boxes, making still another box, only there was furious haste in his movements. He, in his thought, was careering off in other places, even as the carpenter who as he works whistles and thinks of his friend or his enemy, his home or a saloon. And these jolted dreams were never perfect to him afterward, but remained a mass of blurred shapes.

Presently he began to feel the effects of the war atmosphere—a blistering sweat, a sensation that his eyeballs were about to crack like hot stones. A burning roar filled his ears.

Following this came a red rage. He developed the acute exasperation of a pestered animal, a well-meaning cow worried by dogs. He had a mad feeling against his rifle, which could only be used against one life at a time. He wished to rush forward and strangle with his fingers. He craved a power that would enable him to make a world-sweeping gesture and brush all back. His impotency appeared to him, and made his rage into that of a driven beast.

Buried in the smoke of many rifles his anger was directed not so much against the men who he knew were rushing toward him as against the swirling battle phantoms which were choking him, stuffing their smoke robes down his parched throat. He fought frantically for respite for his senses, for air, as a babe being smothered attacks the deadly blankets.

There was a blare of heated rage mingled with a certain expression of intentness on all faces. Many of the men were making low-toned noises with their mouths, and these subdued cheers, snarls, imprecations, prayers, made a wild, barbaric song that went as an undercurrent of sound, strange and chantlike, with the resounding chords of the war march. The man at the youth's elbow was babbling. In it there was something soft and tender like the monologue of a babe. The tall soldier was swearing in a loud voice. From his lips came a black procession of curious oaths. Of a sudden another broke out in a querulous way, like a man who has mislaid his hat. "Well, why don't they support us? Why don't they send supports? Do they think—"

The youth in his battle sleep heard this as one who dozes hears.

There was a singular absence of heroic poses. The men bending and surging in their haste and rage were in every impossible attitude. The steel ramrods clanked and clanged with incessant din as the men pounded them furiously into the hot rifle barrels. The flaps of the cartridge boxes were all unfastened, and bobbed idiotically with each movement. The rifles, once loaded, were jerked to the shoulder and fired without

apparent aim into the smoke or at one of the blurred
and shifting forms which upon the field before the
regiment had been growing larger and larger like pup-
pets under a magician's hands.

The officers, at their intervals, rearward, neglected
to stand in picturesque attitudes. They were bobbing
to and fro roaring directions and encouragements. The
dimensions of their howls were extraordinary. They
expended their lungs with prodigal wills. And often
they nearly stood upon their heads in their anxiety to
observe the enemy on the other side of the tumbling
smoke.

The lieutenant of the youth's company had encountered a soldier who had fled screaming at the first volley of his comrades. Behind the lines these two were
acting a little isolated scene. The man was blubbering
and staring with sheeplike eyes at the lieutenant, who
had seized him by the collar and was pommelling him.
He drove him back into the ranks with many blows.
The soldier went mechanically, dully, with his animal-
like eyes upon the officer. Perhaps there was to him a
divinity expressed in the voice of the other—stern,
hard, with no reflection of fear in it. He tried to reload
his gun, but his shaking hands prevented. The lieutenant was obliged to assist him.

The men dropped here and there like bundles.

The captain of the youth's company had been killed
in an early part of the action. His body lay stretched
out in the position of a tired man resting, but upon
his face there was an astonished and sorrowful look, as
if he thought some friend had done him an ill turn.
The babbling man was grazed by a shot that made the

blood stream widely down his face. He clasped both hands to his head. "Oh!" he said, and ran. Another grunted suddenly as if he had been struck by a club in the stomach. He sat down and gazed ruefully. In his eyes there was mute, indefinite reproach. Further up the line a man, standing behind a tree, had had his knee joint splintered by a ball. Immediately he had dropped his rifle and gripped the tree with both arms. And there he remained, clinging desperately and crying for assistance, that he might withdraw his hold upon the tree.

At last an exultant yell went along the quivering line. The firing dwindled from an uproar to a last vindictive popping. As the smoke slowly eddied away, the youth saw that the charge had been repulsed. The enemy was scattered into reluctant groups. He saw a man climb to the top of the fence, straddle the rail, and fire a parting shot. The waves had receded, leaving bits of dark *débris* upon the ground.

Some in the regiment began to whoop frenziedly. Many were silent. Apparently they were trying to contemplate themselves.

After the fever had left his veins, the youth thought that at last he was going to suffocate. He became aware of the foul atmosphere in which he had been struggling. He was grimy and dripping like a laborer in a foundry. He grasped his canteen and took a long swallow of the warmed water.

A sentence with variations went up and down the line. "Well, we've helt 'em back. We've helt 'em back; derned if we haven't." The men said it blissfully, leering at each other with dirty smiles.

The youth turned to look behind him and off to the right and off to the left. He experienced the joy of a man who at last finds leisure in which to look about him.

Underfoot there were a few ghastly forms motionless. They lay twisted in fantastic contortions. Arms were bent and heads were turned in incredible ways. It seemed that the dead men must have fallen from some great height to get into such positions. They looked to be dumped out upon the ground from the sky.

From a position in the rear of the grove a battery was throwing shells over it. The flash of the guns startled the youth at first. He thought they were aimed directly at him. Through the trees he watched the black figures of the gunners as they worked swiftly and intently. Their labor seemed a complicated thing. He wondered how they could remember its formula in the midst of confusion.

The guns squatted in a row like savage chiefs. They argued with abrupt violence. It was a grim pow-wow. Their busy servants ran hither and thither.

A small procession of wounded men were going drearily toward the rear. It was a flow of blood from the torn body of the brigade.

To the right and to the left were the dark lines of other troops. Far in front he thought he could see lighter masses protruding in points from the forest. They were suggestive of unnumbered thousands.

Once he saw a tiny battery go dashing along the line of the horizon. The tiny riders were beating the tiny horses.

From a sloping hill came the sounds of cheerings and clashes. Smoke welled slowly through the leaves.

Batteries were speaking with thunderous oratorical effort. Here and there were flags, the red in the stripes dominating. They splashed bits of warm color upon the dark lines of troops.

The youth felt the old thrill at the sight of the emblem. They were like beautiful birds strangely undaunted in a storm.

As he listened to the din from the hillside, to a deep pulsating thunder that came from afar to the left, and to the lesser clamors which came from many directions, it occurred to him that they were fighting, too, over there, and over there, and over there. Heretofore he had supposed that all the battle was directly under his nose.

As he gazed around him the youth felt a flash of astonishment at the blue, pure sky and the sun gleaming on the trees and fields. It was surprising that Nature had gone tranquilly on with her golden process in the midst of so much devilment.

The youth awakened slowly. He came gradually back to a position from which he could regard himself. For moments he had been scrutinizing his person in a dazed way as if he had never before seen himself. Then he picked up his cap from the ground. He wriggled in his jacket to make a more comfortable fit, and kneeling relaced his shoe. He thoughtfully mopped his reeking features.

So it was all over at last! The supreme trial had

been passed. The red, formidable difficulties of war
had been vanquished.

He went into an ecstasy of self-satisfaction. He had
the most delightful sensations of his life. Standing as
if apart from himself, he viewed that last scene. He
perceived that the man who had fought thus was magnificent.

He felt that he was a fine fellow. He saw himself
even with those ideals which he had considered as far
beyond him. He smiled in deep gratification.

Upon his fellows he beamed tenderness and good
will. "Gee! ain't it hot, hey?" he said affably to a man
who was polishing his streaming face with his coat-
sleeves.

"You bet!" said the other, grinning sociably. "I
never seen sech dumb hotness." He sprawled out lux-
uriously on the ground. "Gee, yes! An' I hope we don't
have no more fightin' till a week from Monday."

There were some handshakings and deep speeches
with men whose features were familiar, but with whom
the youth now felt the bonds of tied hearts. He helped
a cursing comrade to bind up a wound of the shin.

But, of a sudden, cries of amazement broke out
along the ranks of the new regiment. "Here they come
ag'in! Here they come ag'in!" The man who had
sprawled upon the ground started up and said, "Gosh!"

The youth turned quick eyes upon the field. He dis-
cerned forms begin to swell in masses out of a distant
wood. He again saw the tilted flag speeding forward.

The shells, which had ceased to trouble the regiment for a time, came swirling again, and exploded in

the grass or among the leaves of the trees. They looked to be strange war flowers bursting into fierce bloom.

The men groaned. The luster faded from their eyes. Their smudged countenances now expressed a profound dejection. They moved their stiffened bodies slowly, and watched in sullen mood the frantic approach of the enemy. The slaves toiling in the temple of this god began to feel rebellion at his harsh tasks.

They fretted and complained each to each. "Oh, say, this is too much of a good thing! Why can't somebody send us supports?"

"We ain't never goin' to stand this second banging. I didn't come here to fight the hull damn' rebel army."

There was one who raised a doleful cry. "I wish Bill Smithers had trod on my hand, insteader me treddin' on his'n." The sore joints of the regiment creaked as it painfully floundered into position to repulse.

The youth stared. Surely, he thought, this impossible thing was not about to happen. He waited as if he expected the enemy to suddenly stop, apologize, and retire bowing. It was all a mistake.

But the firing began somewhere on the regimental line and ripped along in both directions. The level sheets of flame developed great clouds of smoke that tumbled and tossed in the mild wind near the ground for a moment, and then rolled through the ranks as through a gate. The clouds were tinged an earthlike yellow in the sunrays and in the shadow were a sorry blue. The flag was sometimes eaten and lost in this mass of vapor, but more often it projected, sun-touched, resplendent.

Into the youth's eyes there came a look that one can see in the orbs of a jaded horse. His neck was quivering with nervous weakness and the muscles of his arms felt numb and bloodless. His hands, too, seemed large and awkward as if he was wearing invisible mittens. And there was a great uncertainty about his knee joints.

The words that comrades had uttered previous to the firing began to recur to him. "Oh, say, this is too much of a good thing! What do they take us for—why don't they send supports? I didn't come here to fight the hull damned rebel army."

He began to exaggerate the endurance, the skill, and the valor of those who were coming. Himself reeling from exhaustion, he was astonished beyond measure at such persistency. They must be machines of steel. It was very gloomy struggling against such affairs, wound up perhaps to fight until sundown.

He slowly lifted his rifle and catching a glimpse of the thick-spread field he blazed at a cantering cluster. He stopped then and began to peer as best he could through the smoke. He caught changing views of the ground covered with men who were all running like pursued imps, and yelling.

To the youth it was an onslaught of redoubtable dragons. He became like the man who lost his legs at the approach of the red and green monster. He waited in a sort of a horrified, listening attitude. He seemed to shut his eyes and wait to be gobbled.

A man near him who up to this time had been working feverishly at his rifle suddenly stopped and ran with howls. A lad whose face had borne an expression of exalted courage, the majesty of him who dares give his life, was, at an instant, smitten abject. He blanched like one who has come to the edge of a cliff at midnight and is suddenly made aware. There was a revelation. He, too, threw down his gun and fled. There was no shame in his face. He ran like a rabbit.

Others began to scamper away through the smoke. The youth turned his head, shaken from his trance by this movement as if the regiment was leaving him behind. He saw the few fleeting forms.

He yelled then with fright and swung about. For a moment, in the great clamor, he was like a proverbial chicken. He lost the direction of safety. Destruction threatened him from all points.

Directly he began to speed toward the rear in great leaps. His rifle and cap were gone. His unbuttoned coat bulged in the wind. The flap of his cartridge box bobbed wildly, and his canteen, by its slender cord, swung out behind. On his face was all the horror of those things which he imagined.

The lieutenant sprang forward bawling. The youth saw his features wrathfully red, and saw him make a dab with his sword. His one thought of the incident was that the lieutenant was a peculiar creature to feel interested in such matters upon this occasion.

He ran like a blind man. Two or three times he fell down. Once he knocked his shoulder so heavily against a tree that he went headlong.

Since he had turned his back upon the fight his fears had been wondrously magnified. Death about to thrust him between the shoulderblades was far more dreadful than death about to smite him between the eyes. When he thought of it later, he conceived the impression that it is better to view the appalling than to be merely within hearing. The noises of the battle were like stones; he believed himself liable to be crushed.

As he ran on he mingled with others. He dimly saw men on his right and on his left, and he heard footsteps behind him. He thought that all the regiment was fleeing, pursued by these ominous crashes.

In his flight the sound of these following footsteps gave him his one meager relief. He felt vaguely that death must make a first choice of the men who were nearest; the initial morsels for the dragons would be then those who were following him. So he displayed the zeal of an insane sprinter in his purpose to keep them in the rear. There was a race.

As he, leading, went across a little field, he found himself in a region of shells. They hurtled over his head with long wild screams. As he listened he imagined them to have rows of cruel teeth that grinned at him. Once one lit before him and the livid lightning of the explosion effectually barred the way in his chosen direction. He grovelled on the ground and then springing up went careering off through some bushes.

He experienced a thrill of amazement when he came within view of a battery in action. The men there seemed to be in conventional moods, altogether unaware of the impending annihilation. The battery was disputing with a distant antagonist and the gunners were wrapped in admiration of their shooting. They were continually bending in coaxing postures over the guns. They seemed to be patting them on the back and encouraging them with words. The guns, stolid and undaunted, spoke with dogged valor.

The precise gunners were coolly enthusiastic. They lifted their eyes every chance to the smoke-wreathed hillock from whence the hostile battery addressed them. The youth pitied them as he ran. Methodical idiots! Machine-like fools! The refined joy of planting shells in the midst of the other battery's formation would appear a little thing when the infantry came swooping out of the woods.

The face of a youthful rider, who was jerking his frantic horse with an abandon of temper he might display in a placid barnyard, was impressed deeply upon his mind. He knew that he looked upon a man who would presently be dead.

Too, he felt a pity for the guns, standing, six good comrades, in a bold row.

He saw a brigade going to the relief of its pestered fellows. He scrambled upon a wee hill and watched it sweeping finely, keeping formation in difficult places. The blue of the line was crusted with steel color, and the brilliant flags projected. Officers were shouting.

The sight also filled him with wonder. The brigade was hurrying briskly to be gulped into the infernal mouths of the war god. What manner of men were they, anyhow? Ah, it was some wondrous breed! Or else they didn't comprehend—the fools.

A furious order caused commotion in the artillery. An officer on a bounding horse made maniacal motions with his arms. The teams went swinging up from the rear, the guns were whirled about, and the battery scampered away. The cannon with their noses poked slantingly at the ground grunted and grumbled like stout men, brave but with objections to hurry.

The youth went on, moderating his pace since he had left the place of noises.

Later he came upon a general of division seated upon a horse that pricked its ears in an interested way at the battle. There was a great gleaming of yellow and patent leather about the saddle and bridle. The quiet man astride looked mouse-colored upon such a splendid charger.

A jingling staff was galloping hither and thither. Sometimes the general was surrounded by horsemen and at other times he was quite alone. He looked to be much harassed. He had the appearance of a business man whose market is swinging up and down.

The youth went slinking around this spot. He went as near as he dared trying to overhear words. Perhaps the general, unable to comprehend chaos, might call upon him for information. And he could tell him. He knew all concerning it. Of a surety the force was in a fix, and any fool could see that if they did not retreat while they had opportunity—why—

He felt that he would like to thrash the general, or at least approach and tell him in plain words exactly what he thought him to be. It was criminal to stay calmly in one spot and make no effort to stay destruction. He loitered in a fever of eagerness for the division commander to apply to him.

As he warily moved about he heard the general call out irritably: "Tompkins, go over an' see Taylor, an' tell him not t' be in such an all-fired hurry; tell him t' halt his brigade in th' edge of th' woods; tell him t' detach a reg'ment—say I think th' center'll break if we don't help it out some; tell him t' hurry up."

A slim youth on a fine chestnut horse caught these swift words from the mouth of his superior. He made his horse bound into a gallop almost from a walk in his haste to go upon his mission. There was a cloud of dust.

A moment later the youth saw the general bounce excitedly in the saddle.

"Yes, by heavens, they have!" The officer leaned forward. His face was aflame with excitement. "Yes, by heavens, they've held 'im! They've held 'im!"

He began blithely to roar at his staff: "We'll wallop 'im now. We'll wallop 'im now. We've got 'em sure." He turned suddenly upon an aid: "Here—you—Jones—quick—ride after Tompkins—see Taylor—tell him t' go in—everlastingly—like blazes—anything."

As another officer sped his horse after the first messenger, the general beamed upon the earth like a sun. In his eyes was a desire to chant a pæan. He kept repeating, "They've held 'em, by heavens!"

His excitement made his horse plunge, and he merrily kicked and swore at it. He held a little carnival of joy on horseback.

The youth cringed as if discovered in a crime. By heavens, they had won after all! The imbecile line had remained and become victors. He could hear cheering.

He lifted himself upon his toes and looked in the direction of the fight. A yellow fog lay wallowing on the treetops. From beneath it came the clatter of musketry. Hoarse cries told of an advance.

He turned away amazed and angry. He felt that he had been wronged.

He had fled, he told himself, because annihilation approached. He had done a good part in saving himself, who was a little piece of the army. He had considered the time, he said, to be one in which it was the duty of every little piece to rescue itself if possible. Later the officers could fit the little pieces together again, and make a battle front. If none of the little pieces were wise enough to save themselves from the flurry of death at such a time, why, then, where would be the army? It was all plain that he had proceeded according to very correct and commendable rules. His actions had been sagacious things. They had been full of strategy. They were the work of a master's legs.

Thoughts of his comrades came to him. The brittle blue line had withstood the blows and won. He grew bitter over it. It seemed that the blind ignorance and stupidity of those little pieces had betrayed him. He had been overturned and crushed by their lack of sense in holding the position, when intelligent deliberation would have convinced them that it was impossible. He, the enlightened man who looks afar in the dark, had fled because of his superior perceptions and knowledge. He felt a great anger against his comrades. He knew it could be proved that they had been fools.

He wondered what they would remark when later he appeared in camp. His mind heard howls of derision. Their density would not enable them to understand his sharper point of view.

He began to pity himself acutely. He was ill used. He was trodden beneath the feet of an iron injustice. He had proceeded with wisdom and from the most righteous motives under heaven's blue only to be frustrated by hateful circumstances.

A dull, animal-like rebellion against his fellows, war in the abstract, and fate grew within him. He shambled along with bowed head, his brain in a tumult of agony and despair. When he looked lowering up, quivering at each sound, his eyes had the expression of those of a criminal who thinks his guilt and his punishment great, and knows that he can find no words; who, through his suffering, thinks that he peers into the core of things and sees that the judgment of man is thistledown in wind.

He went from the fields into a thick wood, as if resolved to bury himself. He wished to get out of hearing of the crackling shots which were to him like voices.

The ground was cluttered with vines and bushes, and the trees grew close, and spread out like bouquets. He was obliged to force his way with much noise. The creepers, catching against his legs, cried out harshly as their sprays were torn from the barks of trees. The swishing saplings tried to make known his presence to the world. He could not conciliate the forest. As he made his way, it was always calling out protestations. When he separated embraces of trees and vines the disturbed foliages waved their arms and turned their face leaves toward him. He dreaded lest these noisy motions and cries should bring men to look at him. So he went far, seeking dark and intricate places.

After a time the sound of musketry grew faint and

the cannon boomed in the distance. The sun, suddenly apparent, blazed among the trees. The insects were making rhythmical noises. They seemed to be grinding their teeth in unison. A woodpecker stuck his impudent head around the side of a tree. A bird flew on light-hearted wing.

Off was the rumble of death. It seemed now that Nature had no ears.

This landscape gave him assurance. A fair field holding life. It was the religion of peace. It would die if its timid eyes were compelled to see blood. He conceived Nature to be a woman with a deep aversion to tragedy.

He threw a pine cone at a jovial squirrel, and he ran with chattering fear. High in a treetop he stopped, and poking his head cautiously from behind a branch, looked down with an air of trepidation.

The youth felt triumphant at this exhibition. There was the law, he said. Nature had given him a sign. The squirrel, immediately upon recognizing danger, had taken to his legs without ado. He did not stand stolidly baring his furry belly to the missile, and die with an upward glance at the sympathetic heavens. On the contrary, he had fled as fast as his legs could carry him; and he was but an ordinary squirrel, too—doubtless no philosopher of his race. The youth wended, feeling that Nature was of his mind. She re-enforced his argument with proofs that lived where the sun shone.

Once he found himself almost into a swamp. He was obliged to walk upon bog tufts, and watch his feet to keep from the oily mire. Pausing at one time to look about him he saw, out at some black water, a small animal pounce in and emerge directly with a gleaming fish.

The youth went again into the deep thickets. The brushed branches made a noise that drowned the sounds of cannon. He walked on, going from obscurity into promises of a greater obscurity.

At length he reached a place where the high, arching boughs made a chapel. He softly pushed the green doors aside and entered. Pine needles were a gentle brown carpet. There was a religious half light.

Near the threshold he stopped, horror-stricken at the sight of a thing.

He was being looked at by a dead man, who was seated with his back against a columnlike tree. The corpse was dressed in a uniform that once had been blue, but was now faded to a melancholy shade of green. The eyes, staring at the youth, had changed to the dull hue to be seen on the side of a dead fish. The mouth was open. Its red had changed to an appalling yellow. Over the gray skin of the face ran little ants. One was trundling some sort of a bundle along the upper lip.

The youth gave a shriek as he confronted the thing. He was for moments turned to stone before it. He remained staring into the liquid-looking eyes. The dead man and the living man exchanged a long look. Then the youth cautiously put one hand behind him and brought it against a tree. Leaning upon this he retreated, step by step, with his face still toward the thing. He feared that if he turned his back the body might spring up and stealthily pursue him.

The branches, pushing against him, threatened to throw him over upon it. His unguided feet, too, caught aggravatingly in brambles; and with it all he received a subtle suggestion to touch the corpse. As he thought of his hand upon it he shuddered profoundly.

At last he burst the bonds which had fastened him to the spot and fled, unheeding the underbrush. He was pursued by a sight of the black ants swarming greedily upon the gray face and venturing horribly near to the eyes.

After a time he paused, and, breathless and panting, listened. He imagined some strange voice would come from the dead throat and squawk after him in horrible menaces.

The trees about the portal of the chapel moved soughingly in a soft wind. A sad silence was upon the little guarding edifice.

The trees began softly to sing a hymn of twilight. The sun sank until slanted bronze rays struck the forest. There was a lull in the noises of insects as if they had bowed their beaks and were making a devotional pause. There was silence save for the chanted chorus of the trees.

Then, upon this stillness, there suddenly broke a tremendous clangor of sounds. A crimson roar came from the distance.

The youth stopped. He was transfixed by this terrific medley of all noises. It was as if worlds were being rended. There was the ripping sound of musketry and the breaking crash of the artillery.

His mind flew in all directions. He conceived the two armies to be at each other panther fashion. He listened for a time. Then he began to run in the direction of the battle. He saw that it was an ironical thing for him to be running thus toward that which he had been at such pains to avoid. But he said, in substance, to himself that if the earth and the moon were about to clash, many persons would doubtless plan to get upon the roofs to witness the collision.

As he ran, he became aware that the forest had stopped its music, as if at last becoming capable of hearing the foreign sounds. The trees hushed and stood motionless. Everything seemed to be listening to the crackle and clatter and ear-shaking thunder. The chorus pealed over the still earth.

It suddenly occurred to the youth that the fight in which he had been was, after all, but perfunctory popping. In the hearing of this present din he was doubtful if he had seen real battle scenes. This uproar explained a celestial battle; it was tumbling hordes a-struggle in the air.

Reflecting, he saw a sort of a humor in the point of view of himself and his fellows during the late encounter. They had taken themselves and the enemy very seriously and had imagined that they were deciding the war. Individuals must have supposed that they were cutting the letters of their names deep into everlasting tablets of brass, or enshrining their reputations for ever in the hearts of their countrymen, while, as to fact, the affair would appear in printed reports under a meek and immaterial title. But he saw that it was

good, else, he said, in battle every one would surely
run save forlorn hopes and their ilk.

He went rapidly on. He wished to come to the edge
of the forest that he might peer out.

As he hastened, there passed through his mind pictures of stupendous conflicts. His accumulated thought
upon such subjects was used to form scenes. The noise
was as the voice of an eloquent being, describing.

Sometimes the brambles formed chains and tried to
hold him back. Trees, confronting him, stretched out
their arms and forbade him to pass. After its previous
hostility this new resistance of the forest filled him
with a fine bitterness. It seemed that Nature could not
be quite ready to kill him.

But he obstinately took roundabout ways, and presently he was where he could see long gray walls of
vapor where lay battle lines. The voices of cannon
shook him. The musketry sounded in long irregular
surges that played havoc with his ears. He stood re-
gardant for a moment. His eyes had an awestruck expression. He gawked in the direction of the fight.

Presently he proceeded again on his forward way.
The battle was like the grinding of an immense and
terrible machine to him. Its complexities and powers,
its grim processes, fascinated him. He must go close and
see it produce corpses.

He came to a fence and clambered over it. On the
far side, the ground was littered with clothes and guns.
A newspaper, folded up, lay in the dirt. A dead soldier
was stretched with his face hidden in his arm. Farther
off there was a group of four or five corpses keeping

mournful company. A hot sun had blazed upon the spot.

In this place the youth felt that he was an invader. This forgotten part of the battleground was owned by the dead men, and he hurried, in the vague apprehension that one of the swollen forms would rise and tell him to begone.

He came finally to a road from which he could see in the distance dark and agitated bodies of troops, smoke-fringed. In the lane was a bloodstained crowd streaming to the rear. The wounded men were cursing, groaning, and wailing. In the air, always, was a mighty swell of sound that it seemed could sway the earth. With the courageous words of the artillery and the spiteful sentences of the musketry mingled red cheers. And from this region of noises came the steady current of the maimed.

One of the wounded men had a shoeful of blood. He hopped like a schoolboy in a game. He was laughing hysterically.

One was swearing that he had been shot in the arm through the commanding general's mismanagement of the army. One was marching with an air imitative of some sublime drum major. Upon his features was an unholy mixture of merriment and agony. As he marched he sang a bit of doggerel in a high and quavering voice:

> "Sing a song 'a vic'try,
>   A pocketful 'a bullets,
> Five an' twenty dead men
>   Baked in a—pie."

Parts of the procession limped and staggered to this tune.

Another had the gray seal of death already upon his face. His lips were curled in hard lines and his teeth were clinched. His hands were bloody from where he had pressed them upon his wound. He seemed to be awaiting the moment when he should pitch headlong. He stalked like the specter of a soldier, his eyes burning with the power of a stare into the unknown.

There were some who proceeded sullenly, full of anger at their wounds, and ready to turn upon anything as an obscure cause.

An officer was carried along by two privates. He was peevish. "Don't joggle so, Johnson, yeh fool," he cried. "Think m' leg is made of iron? If yeh can't carry me decent, put me down an' let someone else do it."

He bellowed at the tottering crowd who blocked the quick march of his bearers. "Say, make way there, can't yeh? Make way, dickens take it all."

They sulkily parted and went to the roadsides. As he was carried past they made pert remarks to him. When he raged in reply and threatened them, they told him to be damned.

The shoulder of one of the tramping bearers knocked heavily against the spectral soldier who was staring into the unknown.

The youth joined this crowd and marched along with it. The torn bodies expressed the awful machinery in which the men had been entangled.

Orderlies and couriers occasionally broke through the throng in the roadway, scattering wounded men right and left, galloping on followed by howls. The melancholy march was continually disturbed by the messengers, and sometimes by bustling batteries that came swinging and thumping down upon them, the officers shouting orders to clear the way.

There was a tattered man, fouled with dust, blood and powder stain from hair to shoes, who trudged quietly at the youth's side. He was listening with eagerness and much humility to the lurid descriptions of a bearded sergeant. His lean features wore an expression of awe and admiration. He was like a listener in a country store to wondrous tales told among the sugar barrels. He eyed the storyteller with unspeakable wonder. His mouth was agape in yokel fashion.

The sergeant, taking note of this, gave pause to his elaborate history while he administered a sardonic comment. "Be keerful, honey, you'll be a-ketchin' flies," he said.

The tattered man shrank back abashed.

After a time he began to sidle near to the youth, and in a different way try to make him a friend. His voice was gentle as a girl's voice and his eyes were pleading. The youth saw with surprise that the soldier had two wounds, one in the head, bound with a blood-soaked rag, and the other in the arm, making that member dangle like a broken bough.

After they had walked together for some time the tattered man mustered sufficient courage to speak. "Was pretty good fight, wa'n't it?" he timidly said. The youth, deep in thought, glanced up at the bloody and grim figure with its lamblike eyes. "What?"

"Was pretty good fight, wa'n't it?"

"Yes," said the youth shortly. He quickened his pace.

But the other hobbled industriously after him. There was an air of apology in his manner, but he evidently thought that he needed only to talk for a time, and the youth would perceive that he was a good fellow.

"Was pretty good fight, wa'n't it?" he began in a small voice, and then he achieved the fortitude to continue. "Dern me if I ever see fellers fight so. Laws, how they did fight! I knowed th' boys'd like when they onct got square at it. Th' boys ain't had no fair chanct up t' now, but this time they showed what they was. I knowed it'd turn out this way. Yeh can't lick them boys. No, sir! They're fighters, they be."

He breathed a deep breath of humble admiration. He had looked at the youth for encouragement several times. He received none, but gradually he seemed to get absorbed in his subject.

"I was talkin' 'cross pickets with a boy from Georgie, onct, an' that boy, he ses, 'Your fellers'll all run like hell when they onct hearn a gun,' he ses. 'Mebbe they will,' I ses, 'but I don't b'lieve none of it,' I ses; 'an' b'jiminey,' I ses back t' 'um, 'mebbe your fellers'll all run like hell when they onct hearn a gun,' I ses. He larfed. Well, they didn't run t'-day, did they, hey? No, sir! They fit, an' fit, an' fit."

His homely face was suffused with a light of love for the army which was to him all things beautiful and powerful.

After a time he turned to the youth. "Where yeh hit, ol' boy?" he asked in a brotherly tone.

The youth felt instant panic at this question, although at first its full import was not borne in upon him.

"What?" he asked.

"Where yeh hit?" repeated the tattered man.

"Why," began the youth, "I—I—that is—why—I—"

He turned away suddenly and slid through the crowd. His brow was heavily flushed, and his fingers were picking nervously at one of his buttons. He bent his head and fastened his eyes studiously upon the button as if it were a little problem.

The tattered man looked after him in astonishment.

The youth fell back in the procession until the tattered soldier was not in sight. Then he started to walk on with the others.

But he was amid wounds. The mob of men was bleeding. Because of the tattered soldier's question he now felt that his shame could be viewed. He was continually casting sidelong glances to see if the men were contemplating the letters of guilt he felt burned into his brow.

At times he regarded the wounded soldiers in an envious way. He conceived persons with torn bodies to be peculiarly happy. He wished that he, too, had a wound, a red badge of courage.

The spectral soldier was at his side like a stalking reproach. The man's eyes were still fixed in a stare into the unknown. His gray, appalling face had attracted attention in the crowd, and men, slowing to his dreary pace, were walking with him. They were discussing his

plight, questioning him and giving him advice. In a
dogged way he repelled them, signing to them to go on
and leave him alone. The shadows of his face were
deepening and his tight lips seemed holding in check
the moan of great despair. There could be seen a certain stiffness in the movements of his body, as if he
were taking infinite care not to arouse the passion of
his wounds. As he went on he seemed always looking
for a place, like one who goes to choose a grave.

Something in the gesture of the man as he waved the
bloody and pitying soldiers away made the youth start
as if bitten. He yelled in horror. Tottering forward he
laid a quivering hand upon the man's arm. As the latter slowly turned his waxlike features toward him, the
youth screamed:

"Gawd! Jim Conklin!"

The tall soldier made a little commonplace smile.
"Hello, Henry," he said.

The youth swayed on his legs and glared strangely.
He stuttered and stammered. "Oh, Jim—oh, Jim—oh,
Jim—"

The tall soldier held out his gory hand. There was
a curious red and black combination of new blood and
old blood upon it. "Where yeh been, Henry?" he asked.
He continued in a monotonous voice. "I thought mebbe yeh got keeled over. There's been thunder t' pay
t'-day. I was worryin' about it a good deal."

The youth still lamented. "Oh, Jim—oh, Jim—oh,
Jim—"

"Yeh know," said the tall soldier, "I was out there."
He made a careful gesture. "An', Lord, what a circus!
An' b'jiminey, I got shot—I got shot. Yes, b'jiminey, I

got shot." He reiterated this fact in a bewildered way, as if he did not know how it came about.

The youth put forth anxious arms to assist him, but the tall soldier went firmly on as if propelled. Since the youth's arrival as a guardian for his friend, the other wounded men had ceased to display much interest. They occupied themselves again in dragging their own tragedies toward the rear.

Suddenly, as the two friends marched on, the tall soldier seemed to be overcome by a terror. His face turned to a semblance of gray paste. He clutched the youth's arm and looked all about him, as if dreading to be overheard. Then he began to speak in a shaking whisper:

"I tell yeh what I'm 'fraid of, Henry—I'll tell yeh what I'm 'fraid of. I'm 'fraid I'll fall down—an' then yeh know—them damned artillery wagons—they like as not'll run over me. That's what I'm 'fraid of—"

The youth cried out to him hysterically: "I'll take care of yeh, Jim! I'll take care of yeh! I swear t'Gawd I will!"

"Sure—will yeh, Henry?" the tall soldier beseeched.

"Yes—yes—I tell yeh—I'll take care of yeh, Jim!" protested the youth. He could not speak accurately because of the gulpings in his throat.

But the tall soldier continued to beg in a lowly way. He now hung babelike to the youth's arm. His eyes rolled in the wildness of his terror. "I was allus a good friend t' yeh, wa'n't I, Henry? I've allus been a pretty good feller, ain't I? An' it ain't much t' ask, is it? Jest t' pull me along outer th' road? I'd do it fer you, wouldn't I, Henry?"

He paused in piteous anxiety to await his friend's reply.

The youth had reached an anguish where the sobs scorched him. He strove to express his loyalty, but he could only make fantastic gestures.

However, the tall soldier seemed suddenly to forget all those fears. He became again the grim, stalking specter of a soldier. He went stonily forward. The youth wished his friend to lean upon him, but the other always shook his head and strangely protested. "No—no—no—leave me be—leave me be—"

His look was fixed again upon the unknown. He moved with mysterious purpose, and all of the youth's offers he brushed aside. "No—no—leave me be—leave me be—"

The youth had to follow.

Presently the latter heard a voice talking softly near his shoulder. Turning he saw that it belonged to the tattered soldier. "Ye'd better take 'im outa th' road, pardner. There's a batt'ry comin' helitywhoop down th' road an' he'll git runned over. He's a goner anyhow in about five minutes—yeh kin see that. Ye'd better take 'im outa th' road. Where th' blazes does he git his stren'th from?"

"Lord knows!" cried the youth. He was shaking his hands helplessly.

He ran forward presently and grasped the tall soldier by the arm. "Jim! Jim!" he coaxed, "come with me."

The tall soldier weakly tried to wrench himself free. "Huh," he said vacantly. He stared at the youth for a moment. At last he spoke as if dimly comprehending. "Oh! Inteh th' fields? Oh!"

He started blindly through the grass.

The youth turned once to look at the lashing riders and jouncing guns of the battery. He was startled from this view by a shrill outcry from the tattered man.

"Gawd! He's runnin'!"

Turning his head swiftly, the youth saw his friend running in a staggering and stumbling way toward a little clump of bushes. His heart seemed to wrench itself almost free from his body at this sight. He made a noise of pain. He and the tattered man began a pursuit. There was a singular race.

When he overtook the tall soldier he began to plead with all the words he could find. "Jim—Jim—what are you doing—what makes you do this way—you'll hurt yourself."

The same purpose was in the tall soldier's face. He protested in a dulled way, keeping his eyes fastened on the mystic place of his intentions. "No—no—don't tech me—leave me be—leave me be—"

The youth, aghast and filled with wonder at the tall soldier, began quaveringly to question him. "Where yeh goin', Jim? What you thinking about? Where you going? Tell me, won't you, Jim?"

The tall soldier faced about as upon relentless pursuers. In his eyes there was a great appeal. "Leave me be, can't yeh? Leave me be fer a minnit."

The youth recoiled. "Why, Jim," he said, in a dazed way, "what's the matter with you?"

The tall soldier turned and, lurching dangerously,

went on. The youth and the tattered soldier followed, sneaking as if whipped, feeling unable to face the stricken man if he should again confront them. They began to have thoughts of a solemn ceremony. There was something rite-like in these movements of the doomed soldier. And there was a resemblance in him to a devotee of a mad religion, blood-sucking, muscle-wrenching, bone-crushing. They were awed and afraid. They hung back lest he have at command a dreadful weapon.

At last, they saw him stop and stand motionless. Hastening up, they perceived that his face wore an expression telling that he had at last found the place for which he had struggled. His spare figure was erect; his bloody hands were quietly at his side. He was waiting with patience for something that he had come to meet. He was at the rendezvous. They paused and stood, expectant.

There was a silence.

Finally, the chest of the doomed soldier began to heave with a strained motion. It increased in violence until it was as if an animal was within and was kicking and tumbling furiously to be free.

This spectacle of gradual strangulation made the youth writhe, and once as his friend rolled his eyes, he saw something in them that made him sink wailing to the ground. He raised his voice in a last supreme call.

"Jim—Jim—Jim—"

The tall soldier opened his lips and spoke. He made a gesture. "Leave me be—don't tech me—leave me be—"

There was another silence while he waited.

Suddenly, his form stiffened and straightened. Then

it was shaken by a prolonged ague. He stared into space. To the two watchers there was a curious and profound dignity in the firm lines of his awful face.

He was invaded by a creeping strangeness that slowly enveloped him. For a moment the tremor of his legs caused him to dance a sort of hideous hornpipe. His arms beat wildly about his head in expression of imp-like enthusiasm.

His tall figure stretched itself to its full height. There was a slight rending sound. Then it began to swing forward, slow and straight, in the manner of a falling tree. A swift muscular contortion made the left shoulder strike the ground first.

The body seemed to bounce a little way from the earth. "God!" said the tattered soldier.

The youth had watched, spellbound, this ceremony at the place of meeting. His face had been twisted into an expression of every agony he had imagined for his friend.

He now sprang to his feet and, going closer, gazed upon the pastelike face. The mouth was open and the teeth showed in a laugh.

As the flap of the blue jacket fell away from the body, he could see that the side looked as if it had been chewed by wolves.

The youth turned, with sudden, livid rage, toward the battlefield. He shook his fist. He seemed about to deliver a philippic.

"Hell—"

The red sun was pasted in the sky like a fierce wafer.

1895

From DRUM-TAPS

WALT WHITMAN

Beat! Beat! Drums!

Beat! beat! drums—blow! bugles! blow!
Through the windows—through doors—burst like a
    ruthless force,
Into the solemn church, and scatter the congregation,
Into the school where the scholar is studying;
Leave not the bridegroom quiet—no happiness must he
    have now with his bride,
Nor the peaceful farmer any peace, ploughing his field
    or gathering his grain,
So fierce you whirr and pound you drums—so shrill
    you bugles blow.

Beat! beat! drums—blow! bugles! blow!
Over the traffic of cities—over the rumble of wheels in
    the streets;
Are beds prepared for sleepers at night in the houses?
    no sleepers must sleep in those beds,
No bargainers' bargains by day—no brokers or specu-
    lators—would they continue?
Would the talkers be talking? would the singer at-
    tempt to sing?

Would the lawyers rise in the court to state his case be-
    fore the judge?
Then rattle quicker, heavier drums—you bugles wilder
    blow.

Beat! beat! drums—blow! bugles! blow!
Make no parley—stop for no expostulation,
Mind not the timid—mind not the weeper or prayer,
Mind not the old man beseeching the young man,
Let not the child's voice be heard, nor the mother's en-
    treaties,
Make even the trestles to shake the dead where they lie
    awaiting the hearses,
So strong you thump O terrible drums—so loud you
    bugles blow.

Cavalry Crossing a Ford

A line in long array where they wind betwixt green
    islands,
They take a serpentine course, their arms flash in the
    sun—hark to the musical clank,
Behold the silvery river, in it the splashing horses
    loitering stop to drink,
Behold the brown-faced men, each group, each person
    a picture, the negligent rest on the saddles,
Some emerge on the opposite bank, others are just en-
    tering the ford—while,
Scarlet and blue and snowy white,
The guidon flags flutter gayly in the wind.

Vigil Strange I Kept on the Field One Night

Vigil strange I kept on the field one night;
When you my son and my comrade dropt at my side
    that day,
One look I but gave which your dear eyes return'd
    with a look I shall never forget,
One touch of your hand to mine O boy, reach'd up as
    you lay on the ground,
Then onward I sped in the battle, the even-contested
    battle,
Till late in the night reliev'd to the place at last again
    I made my way,
Found you in death so cold dear comrade, found your
    body son of responding kisses, (never again on
    earth responding,)
Bared your face in the starlight, curious the scene,
    cool blew the moderate night-wind,
Long there and then in vigil I stood, dimly around me
    the battle-field spreading,
Vigil wondrous and vigil sweet there in the fragrant
    silent night,
But not a tear fell, not even a long-drawn sigh, long,
    long I gazed,
Then on the earth partially reclining sat by your side
    leaning my chin in my hands,
Passing sweet hours, immortal and mystic hours with
    you dearest comrade—not a tear, not a word,
Vigil of silence, love and death, vigil for you my son
    and my soldier,

As onward silently stars aloft, eastward new ones up-
    ward stole,
Vigil final for you brave boy, (I could not save you,
    swift was your death,
I faithfully loved you and cared for you living, I
    think we shall surely meet again,)
Till at latest lingering of the night, indeed just as the
    dawn appear'd,
My comrade I wrapt in his blanket, envelop'd well his
    form,
Folded the blanket well, tucking it carefully over head
    and carefully under feet,
And there and then and bathed by the rising sun, my
    son in his grave, in his rude-dug grave I deposited,
Ending my vigil strange with that, vigil of night and
    battle-field dim,
Vigil for boy of responding kisses, (never again on
    earth responding,)
Vigil for comrade swiftly slain, vigil I never forget,
    how as day brighten'd,
I rose from the chill ground and folded my soldier well
    in his blanket,
And buried him where he fell.

    A Sight in Camp in the
    Daybreak Gray and Dim

A sight in camp in the daybreak gray and dim,
As from my tent I emerge so early sleepless,
As slow I walk in the cool fresh air the path near by
    the hospital tent,

Three forms I see on stretchers lying, brought out there
    untended lying,
Over each the blanket spread, ample brownish woolen
    blanket,
Gray and heavy blanket, folding, covering all.

Curious I halt and silent stand,
Then with light fingers I from the face of the nearest
    the first just lift the blanket;
Who are you elderly man so gaunt and grim, with
    well-gray'd hair, and flesh all sunken about the
    eyes?
Who are you my dear comrade?

Then to the second I step—and who are you my child
    and darling?
Who are you sweet boy with cheeks yet blooming?

Then to the third—a face nor child nor old, very calm,
    as of beautiful yellow-white ivory;
Young man I think I know you—I think this face is the
    face of the Christ himself,
Dead and divine and brother of all, and here again he
    lies.

Look Down Fair Moon

Look down fair moon and bathe this scene,
Pour softly down night's nimbus floods on faces ghastly,
    swollen, purple,
On the dead on their backs with arms toss'd wide,
Pour down your unstinted nimbus sacred moon.

Reconciliation

Word over all, beautiful as the sky,
Beautiful that war and all its deeds of carnage must in
    time be utterly lost,
That the hands of the sisters Death and Night inces-
    santly softly wash again, and ever again, this soil'd
    world;
For my enemy is dead, a man divine as myself is dead,
I look where he lies white-faced and still in the coffin—
    I draw near,
Bend down and touch lightly with my lips the white
    face in the coffin.

1865

AN OCCURRENCE AT OWL CREEK BRIDGE

AMBROSE BIERCE

A man stood upon a railroad bridge in northern Alabama, looking down into the swift water twenty feet below. The man's hands were behind his back, the wrists bound with a cord. A rope closely encircled his neck. It was attached to a stout cross-timber above his head and the slack fell to the level of his knees. Some loose boards laid upon the sleepers supporting the metals of the railway supplied a footing for him and his executioners—two private soldiers of the Federal army, directed by a sergeant who in civil life may have been a deputy sheriff. At a short remove upon the same temporary platform was an officer in the uniform of his rank, armed. He was a captain. A sentinel at each end of the bridge stood with his rifle in the position known as 'support,' that is to say, vertical in front of the left shoulder, the hammer resting on the forearm thrown straight across the chest—a formal and unnatural position, enforcing an erect carriage of the body. It did not appear to be the duty of these two men to know what was occurring at the centre of the bridge; they merely blockaded the two ends of the foot planking that traversed it.

Beyond one of the sentinels nobody was in sight; the railroad ran straight away into a forest for a hundred yards, then, curving, was lost to view. Doubtless there was an outpost farther along. The other bank of the stream was open ground—a gentle acclivity topped with a stockade of vertical tree trunks, loop-holed for rifles, with a single embrasure through which protruded the muzzle of a brass cannon commanding the bridge. Midway of the slope between bridge and fort were the spectators—a single company of infantry in line, at 'parade rest,' the butts of the rifles on the ground, the barrels inclining slightly backward against the right shoulder, the hands crossed upon the stock. A lieutenant stood at the right of the line, the point of his sword upon the ground, his left hand resting upon his right. Excepting the group of four at the centre of the bridge, not a man moved. The company faced the bridge, staring stonily, motionless. The sentinels, facing the banks of the stream, might have been statues to adorn the bridge. The captain stood with folded arms, silent, observing the work of his subordinates, but making no sign. Death is a dignitary who when he comes announced is to be received with formal manifestations of respect, even by those most familiar with him. In the code of military etiquette silence and fixity are forms of deference.

The man who was engaged in being hanged was apparently about thirty-five years of age. He was a civilian, if one might judge from his habit, which was that of a planter. His features were good—a straight nose, firm mouth, broad forehead, from which his long, dark hair was combed straight back, falling behind his ears to the collar of his well-fitting frock-coat. He wore a mustache and pointed beard, but no whiskers; his eyes were large and dark gray, and had a kindly expression which one would hardly have expected in one whose neck was in the hemp. Evidently this was no vulgar assassin. The liberal military code makes provision for hanging many kinds of persons, and gentlemen are not excluded.

The preparations being complete, the two private soldiers stepped aside and each drew away the plank upon which he had been standing. The sergeant turned to the captain, saluted and placed himself immediately behind that officer, who in turn moved apart one pace. These movements left the condemned man and the sergeant standing on the two ends of the same plank, which spanned three of the cross-ties of the bridge. The end upon which the civilian stood almost, but not quite, reached a fourth. This plank had been held in place by the weight of the captain; it was now held by that of the sergeant. At a signal from the former the latter would step aside, the plank would tilt and the condemned man go down between two ties. The arrangement commended itself to his judgment as simple and effective. His face had not been covered nor his eyes bandaged. He looked a moment at his 'unsteadfast footing,' then let his gaze wander to the swirling water of the stream racing madly beneath his feet. A piece of dancing driftwood caught his attention and his eyes followed it down the current. How slowly it appeared to move! What a sluggish stream!

He closed his eyes in order to fix his last thoughts upon his wife and children. The water, touched to gold by the early sun, the brooding mists under the banks at some distance down the stream, the fort, the soldiers, the piece of drift—all had distracted him. And now he became conscious of a new disturbance. Striking through the thought of his dear ones was a sound which he could neither ignore nor understand, a sharp, distinct, metallic percussion like the stroke of a blacksmith's hammer upon the anvil; it had the same ringing quality. He wondered what it was, and whether immeasurably distant or near by—it seemed both. Its recurrence was regular, but as slow as the tolling of a death knell. He awaited each stroke with impatience and—he knew not why—apprehension. The intervals of silence grew progressively longer; the delays became maddening. With their greater infrequency the sounds increased in strength and sharpness. They hurt his ear like the thrust of a knife; he feared he would shriek. What he heard was the ticking of his watch.

He unclosed his eyes and saw again the water below him. 'If I could free my hands,' he thought, 'I might throw off the noose and spring into the stream. By diving I could evade the bullets and, swimming vigorously, reach the bank, take to the woods and get away home. My home, thank God, is as yet outside their lines; my wife and little ones are still beyond the invader's farthest advance.'

As these thoughts, which have here to be set down in words, were flashed into the doomed man's brain rather than evolved from it, the captain nodded to the sergeant. The sergeant stepped aside.

Peyton Farquhar was a well-to-do planter, of an old and highly respected Alabama family. Being a slave owner and, like other slave owners, a politician he was naturally an original secessionist and ardently devoted to the Southern cause. Circumstances of an imperious nature, which it is unnecessary to relate here, had prevented him from taking service with the gallant army that had fought the disastrous campaigns ending with the fall of Corinth, and he chafed under the inglorious restraint, longing for the release of his energies, the larger life of the soldier, the opportunity for distinction. That opportunity, he felt, would come, as it comes to all in war time. Meanwhile he did what he could. No service was too humble for him to perform in aid of the South, no adventure too perilous for him to undertake if consistent with the character of a civilian who was at heart a soldier, and who in good faith and without too much qualification assented to at least a part of the frankly villainous dictum that all is fair in love and war.

One evening while Farquhar and his wife were sitting on a rustic bench near the entrance to his grounds, a gray-clad soldier rode up to the gate and asked for a drink of water. Mrs. Farquhar was only too happy to serve him with her own white hands. While she was fetching the water her husband approached the dusty horseman and inquired eagerly for news from the front.

'The Yanks are repairing the railroads,' said the man,

'and are getting ready for another advance. They have reached the Owl Creek bridge, put it in order and built a stockade on the north bank. The commandant has issued an order, which is posted everywhere, declaring that any civilian caught interfering with the railroad, its bridges, tunnels or trains will be summarily hanged. I saw the order.'

'How far is it to the Owl Creek bridge?' Farquhar asked.

'About thirty miles.'

'Is there no force on this side the creek?'

'Only a picket post half a mile out, on the railroad, and a single sentinel at this end of the bridge.'

'Suppose a man—a civilian and student of hanging— should elude the picket post and perhaps get the better of the sentinel,' said Farquhar, smiling, 'what could he accomplish?'

The soldier reflected. 'I was there a month ago,' he replied. 'I observed that the flood of last winter had lodged a great quantity of driftwood against the wooden pier at this end of the bridge. It is now dry and would burn like tow.'

The lady had now brought the water, which the soldier drank. He thanked her ceremoniously, bowed to her husband and rode away. An hour later, after nightfall, he repassed the plantation, going northward in the direction from which he had come. He was a Federal scout.

As Peyton Farquhar fell straight downward through the bridge he lost consciousness and was as one already

dead. From this state he was awakened—ages later, it
seemed to him—by the pain of a sharp pressure upon
his throat, followed by a sense of suffocation. Keen,
poignant agonies seemed to shoot from his neck downward through every fibre of his body and limbs. These
pains appeared to flash along well-defined lines of
ramification and to beat with an inconceivably rapid
periodicity. They seemed like streams of pulsating fire
heating him to an intolerable temperature. As to his
head, he was conscious of nothing but a feeling of ful-
ness—of congestion. These sensations were unaccom-
panied by thought. The intellectual part of his nature
was already effaced; he had power only to feel, and feeling was torment. He was conscious of motion. Encom-
passed in a luminous cloud, of which he was now
merely the fiery heart, without material substance, he
swung through unthinkable arcs of oscillation, like a
vast pendulum.

Then all at once, with terrible suddenness, the light
about him shot upward with the noise of a loud plash;
a frightful roaring was in his ears, and all was cold and
dark. The power of thought was restored; he knew that
the rope had broken and he had fallen into the stream.
There was no additional strangulation; the noose
about his neck was already suffocating him and kept
the water from his lungs. To die of hanging at the bottom of a river!—the idea seemed to him ludicrous. He
opened his eyes in the darkness and saw above him a
gleam of light, but how distant, how inaccessible! He
was still sinking, for the light became fainter and
fainter until it was a mere glimmer. Then it began to
grow and brighten, and he knew that he was rising to-

ward the surface—knew it with reluctance, for he was now very comfortable. 'To be hanged and drowned,' he thought, 'that is not so bad; but I do not wish to be shot. No; I will not be shot; that is not fair.'

He was not conscious of an effort, but a sharp pain in his wrist apprised him that he was trying to free his hands. He gave the struggle his attention, as an idler might observe the feat of a juggler, without interest in the outcome. What splendid effort! What magnificent, what superhuman strength! Ah, that was a fine endeavor! Bravo! The cord fell away; his arms parted and floated upward, the hands dimly seen on each side in the growing light. He watched them with a new interest as first one and then the other pounced upon the noose at his neck. They tore it away and thrust it fiercely aside, its undulations resembling those of a water-snake. 'Put it back, put it back!' He thought he shouted these words to his hands, for the undoing of the noose had been succeeded by the direst pang that he had yet experienced. His neck ached horribly; his brain was on fire; his heart, which had been fluttering faintly, gave a great leap, trying to force itself out at his mouth. His whole body was racked and wrenched with an insupportable anguish! But his disobedient hands gave no heed to the command. They beat the water vigorously with quick, downward strokes, forcing him to the surface. He felt his head emerge; his eyes were blinded by the sunlight; his chest expanded convulsively, and with a supreme and crowning agony his lungs engulfed a great draught of air, which instantly he expelled in a shriek!

He was now in full possession of his physical senses.

They were, indeed, preternaturally keen and alert. Something in the awful disturbance of his organic system had so exalted and refined them that they made record of things never before perceived. He felt the ripples upon his face and heard their separate sounds as they struck. He looked at the forest on the bank of the stream, saw the individual trees, the leaves and the veining of each leaf—saw the very insects upon them: the locusts, the brilliant-bodied flies, the gray spiders stretching their webs from twig to twig. He noted the prismatic colors in all the dewdrops upon a million blades of grass. The humming of the gnats that danced above the eddies of the stream, the beating of the dragon-flies' wings, the strokes of the water-spiders' legs, like oars which had lifted their boat—all these made audible music. A fish slid along beneath his eyes and he heard the rush of its body parting the water.

He had come to the surface facing down the stream; in a moment the visible world seemed to wheel slowly round, himself the pivotal point, and he saw the bridge, the fort, the soldiers upon the bridge, the captain, the sergeant, the two privates, his executioners. They were in silhouette against the blue sky. They shouted and gesticulated, pointing at him. The captain had drawn his pistol, but did not fire; the others were unarmed. Their movements were grotesque and horrible, their forms gigantic.

Suddenly he heard a sharp report and something struck the water smartly within a few inches of his head, spattering his face with spray. He heard a second report, and saw one of the sentinels with his rifle at his shoulder, a light cloud of blue smoke rising from the muzzle. The man in the water saw the eye of the man on the bridge gazing into his own through the sights of the rifle. He observed that it was a gray eye and remembered having read that gray eyes were keenest, and that all famous marksmen had them. Nevertheless, this one had missed.

A counter-swirl had caught Farquhar and turned him half round; he was again looking into the forest on the bank opposite the fort. The sound of a clear, high voice in a monotonous singsong now rang out behind him and came across the water with a distinctness that pierced and subdued all other sounds, even the beating of the ripples in his ears. Although no soldier, he had frequented camps enough to know the dread significance of that deliberate, drawing, aspirated chant; the lieutenant on shore was taking a part in the morning's work. How coldly and pitilessly—with what an even, calm intonation, presaging and enforcing tranquillity in the men—with what accurately measured intervals fell those cruel words:

'Attention, company! ... Shoulder arms! ... Ready! ... Aim! ... Fire!'

Farquhar dived—dived as deeply as he could. The water roared in his ears like the voice of Niagara, yet he heard the dulled thunder of the volley and, rising again toward the surface, met shining bits of metal, singularly flattened, oscillating slowly downward. Some of them touched him on the face and hands, then fell away, continuing their descent. One lodged between his collar and neck; it was uncomfortably warm and he snatched it out.

As he rose to the surface, gasping for breath, he saw

that he had been a long time under water; he was perceptibly farther down stream—nearer to safety. The soldiers had almost finished reloading; the metal ramrods flashed all at once in the sunshine as they were drawn from the barrels, turned in the air, and thrust into their sockets. The two sentinels fired again, independently and ineffectually.

The hunted man saw all this over his shoulder; he was now swimming vigorously with the current. His brain was as energetic as his arms and legs; he thought with the rapidity of lightning.

'The officer,' he reasoned, 'will not make that martinet's error a second time. It is as easy to dodge a volley as a single shot. He has probably already given the command to fire at will. God help me, I cannot dodge them all!'

An appalling plash within two yards of him was followed by a loud, rushing sound, *diminuendo,* which seemed to travel back through the air to the fort and died in an explosion which stirred the very river to its deeps! A rising sheet of water curved over him, fell down upon him, blinded him, strangled him! The cannon had taken a hand in the game. As he shook his head free from the commotion of the smitten water he heard the deflected shot humming through the air ahead, and in an instant it was cracking and smashing the branches in the forest beyond.

'They will not do that again,' he thought, 'the next time they will use a charge of grape. I must keep my eye upon the gun; the smoke will apprise me—the report arrives too late; it lags behind the missile. That is a good gun.'

Suddenly he felt himself whirled round and round—spinning like a top. The water, the banks, the forests, the now distant bridge, fort and men—all were commingled and blurred. Objects were represented by their colors only; circular horizontal streaks of color—that was all he saw. He had been caught in a vortex and was being whirled on with a velocity of advance and gyration that made him giddy and sick. In a few moments he was flung upon the gravel at the foot of the left bank of the stream—the southern bank—and behind a projecting point which concealed him from his enemies. The sudden arrest of his motion, the abrasion of one of his hands on the gravel, restored him, and he wept with delight. He dug his fingers into the sand, threw it over himself in handfuls and audibly blessed it. It looked like diamonds, rubies, emeralds; he could think of nothing beautiful which it did not resemble. The trees upon the bank were giant garden plants; he noted a definite order in their arrangement, inhaled the fragrance of their blooms. A strange, roseate light shone through the spaces among their trunks and the wind made in their branches the music of æolian harps. He had no wish to perfect his escape—was content to remain in that enchanting spot until retaken.

A whiz and rattle of grapeshot among the branches high above his head roused him from his dream. The baffled cannoneer had fired him a random farewell. He sprang to his feet, rushed up the sloping bank, and plunged into the forest.

All that day he traveled, laying his course by the rounding sun. The forest seemed interminable; nowhere did he discover a break in it, not even a woodman's road. He had not known that he lived in so wild a region. There was something uncanny in the revelation.

By nightfall he was fatigued, footsore, famishing. The thought of his wife and children urged him on. At last he found a road which led him in what he knew to be the right direction. It was as wide and straight as a city street, yet it seemed untraveled. No fields bordered it, no dwelling anywhere. Not so much as the barking of a dog suggested human habitation. The black bodies of the trees formed a straight wall on both sides, terminating on the horizon in a point, like a diagram in a lesson in perspective. Overhead, as he looked up through this rift in the wood, shone great golden stars looking unfamiliar and grouped in strange constellations. He was sure they were arranged in some order which had a secret and malign significance. The wood on either side was full of singular noises, among which—once, twice, and again—he distinctly heard whispers in an unknown tongue.

His neck was in pain and lifting his hand to it he found it horribly swollen. He knew that it had a circle of black where the rope had bruised it. His eyes felt congested; he could no longer close them. His tongue was swollen with thirst; he relieved its fever by thrusting it forward from between his teeth into the cold air. How softly the turf had carpeted the untraveled avenue —he could no longer feel the roadway beneath his feet!

Doubtless, despite his suffering, he had fallen asleep while walking, for now he sees another scene—perhaps he has merely recovered from a delirium. He stands at the gate of his own home. All is as he left it, and all bright and beautiful in the morning sunshine. He must have traveled the entire night. As he pushes open the gate and passes up the wide white walk, he sees a flutter of female garments; his wife, looking fresh and cool and sweet, steps down from the veranda to meet him. At the bottom of the steps she stands waiting, with a smile of ineffable joy, an attitude of matchless grace and dignity. Ah, how beautiful she is! He springs forward with extended arms. As he is about to clasp her he feels a stunning blow upon the back of the neck; a blinding white light blazes all about him with a sound like the shock of a cannon—then all is darkness and silence!

Peyton Farquhar was dead; his body, with a broken neck, swung gently from side to side beneath the timbers of the Owl Creek bridge.

1891

DO NOT WEEP, MAIDEN, FOR WAR IS KIND

STEPHEN CRANE

Do not weep, maiden, for war is kind.
Because your lover threw wild hands toward the sky
And the affrighted steed ran on alone,
Do not weep.
War is kind.

    Hoarse, booming drums of the regiment,
    Little souls who thirst for fight,
    These men were born to drill and die.
    The unexplained glory flies above them,
    Great is the battle-god, great, and his kingdom—
    A field where a thousand corpses lie.

Do not weep, babe, for war is kind.
Because your father tumbled in the yellow trenches,
Raged at his breast, gulped and died,
Do not weep.
War is kind.

    Swift blazing flag of the regiment,
    Eagle with crest of red and gold,
    These men were born to drill and die.
    Point for them the virtue of slaughter,

Make plain to them the excellence of killing
And a field where a thousand corpses lie.

Mother whose heart hung humble as a button
On the bright splendid shroud of your son,
Do not weep.
War is kind.

1895

THE WAR PRAYER

MARK TWAIN

It was a time of great and exalting excitement. The country was up in arms, the war was on, in every breast burned the holy fire of patriotism; the drums were beating, the bands playing, the toy pistols popping, the bunched firecrackers hissing and spluttering; on every hand and far down the receding and fading spread of roofs and balconies a fluttering wilderness of flags flashed in the sun; daily the young volunteers marched down the wide avenue gay and fine in their new uniforms, the proud fathers and mothers and sisters and sweethearts cheering them with voices choked with happy emotion as they swung by; nightly the packed mass meetings listened, panting, to patriot oratory which stirred the deepest deeps of their hearts, and which they interrupted at briefest intervals with cyclones of applause, the tears running down their cheeks the while; in the churches the pastors preached devotion to flag and country, and invoked the God of Battles, beseeching His aid in our good cause in outpouring of fervid eloquence which moved every listener. It was indeed a glad and gracious time, and the half dozen rash spirits that ventured to disapprove of the war and cast a doubt upon its righteousness

straightway got such a stern and angry warning that
for their personal safety's sake they quickly shrank out
of sight and offended no more in that way.

Sunday morning came—next day the battalions would
leave for the front; the church was filled; the volunteers were there, their young faces alight with martial
dreams—visions of the stern advance, the gathering mo-
mentum, the rushing charge, the flashing sabers, the
flight of the foe, the tumult, the enveloping smoke, the
fierce pursuit, the surrender!—then home from the
war, bronzed heroes, welcomed, adored, submerged
in golden seas of glory! With the volunteers sat their
dear ones, proud, happy, and envied by the neighbors
and friends who had no sons and brothers to send
forth to the field of honor, there to win for the flag, or,
failing, die the noblest of noble deaths. The service
proceeded; a war chapter from the Old Testament was
read; the first prayer was said; it was followed by an
organ burst that shook the building, and with one
impulse the house rose, with glowing eyes and beating
hearts, and poured out that tremendous invocation—

"God the all-terrible! Thou who ordainest,
  Thunder thy clarion and lightning thy sword!"

Then came the "long" prayer. None could remember
the like of it for passionate pleading and moving and
beautiful language. The burden of its supplication
was, that an ever-merciful and benignant Father of
us all would watch over our noble young soldiers, and
aid, comfort, and encourage them in their patriotic
work; bless them, shield them in the day of battle and

the hour of peril, bear them in His mighty hand, make them strong and confident, invincible in the bloody onset; help them to crush the foe, grant to them and to their flag and country imperishable honor and glory—

An aged stranger entered and moved with slow and noiseless step up the main aisle, his eyes fixed upon the minister, his long body clothed in a robe that reached to his feet, his head bare, his white hair descending in a frothy cataract to his shoulders, his seamy face unnaturally pale, pale even to ghastliness. With all eyes following him and wondering, he made his silent way; without pausing, he ascended to the preacher's side and stood there, waiting. With shut lids the preacher, unconscious of his presence, continued his moving prayer, and at last finished it with the words, uttered in fervent appeal, "Bless our arms, grant us the victory, O Lord our God, Father and Protector of our land and flag!"

The stranger touched his arm, motioned him to step aside—which the startled minister did—and took his place. During some moments he surveyed the spellbound audience with solemn eyes, in which burned an uncanny light; then in a deep voice he said:

"I come from the Throne—bearing a message from Almighty God!" The words smote the house with a shock; if the stranger perceived it he gave no attention. "He has heard the prayer of His servant your shepherd, and will grant it if such shall be your desire after I, His messenger, shall have explained to you its import—that is to say, its full import. For it is like unto many of the prayers of men, in that it asks for more than he who utters it is aware of—except he pause and think.

"God's servant and yours has prayed his prayer. Has he paused and taken thought? Is it one prayer? No, it is two—one uttered, the other not. Both have reached the ear of Him Who heareth all supplications, the spoken and the unspoken. Ponder this—keep it in mind. If you would beseech a blessing upon yourself, beware! lest without intent you invoke a curse upon a neighbor at the same time. If you pray for the blessing of rain upon your crop which needs it, by that act you are possibly praying for a curse upon some neighbor's crop which may not need rain and can be injured by it.

"You have heard your servant's prayer—the uttered part of it. I am commissioned of God to put into words the other part of it—that part which the pastor—and also you in your hearts—fervently prayed silently. And ignorantly and unthinkingly? God grant that it was so! You heard these words: 'Grant us the victory, O Lord our God!' That is sufficient. The *whole* of the uttered prayer is compact into those pregnant words. Elaborations were not necessary. When you have prayed for victory you have prayed for many unmentioned results which follow victory—*must* follow it, cannot help but follow it. Upon the listening spirit of God the Father fell also the unspoken part of the prayer. He commandeth me to put it into words. Listen!

"O Lord our Father, our young patriots, idols of our hearts, go forth to battle—be Thou near them! With them—in spirit—we also go forth from the sweet peace of our beloved firesides to smite the foe. O Lord

our God, help us to tear their soldiers to bloody shreds
with our shells; help us to cover their smiling fields
with the pale forms of their patriot dead; help us to
drown the thunder of the guns with the shrieks of
their wounded, writhing in pain; help us to lay waste
their humble homes with a hurricane of fire; help us
to wring the hearts of their unoffending widows with
unavailing grief; help us to turn them out roofless with
their little children to wander unfriended the wastes
of their desolated land in rags and hunger and thirst,
sports of the sun flames of summer and the icy winds
of winter, broken in spirit, worn with travail, implor-
ing Thee for the refuge of the grave and denied it—
for our sakes who adore Thee, Lord, blast their hopes,
blight their lives, protract their bitter pilgrimage, make
heavy their steps, water their way with their tears, stain
the white snow with the blood of their wounded feet!
We ask it, in the spirit of love, of Him Who is the
Source of Love, and Who is the ever-faithful refuge
and friend of all that are sore beset and seek His aid
with humble and contrite hearts. Amen."

(After a pause.) "Ye have prayed it; if ye still desire
it, speak! The messenger of the Most High waits."

It was believed afterward that the man was a luna-
tic, because there was no sense in what he said.

1905

FULL MOON: NEW GUINEA

KARL SHAPIRO

These nights we fear the aspects of the moon,
Sleep lightly in the radiance falling clear
On palms and ferns and hills and us; for soon
The small burr of the bombers in our ear
Tickles our rest; we rise as from a nap
And take our helmets absently and meet,
Prepared for any spectacle or mishap,
At trenches fresh and narrow at our feet.

Look up, look up, and wait and breathe. These nights
We fear Orion and the Cross. The crowd
Of deadly insects caught in our long lights
Glitter and seek to burrow in a cloud
Soft-mined with high explosive. Breathe and wait,
The bombs are falling darkly for our fate.

1945

THE GUN

KARL SHAPIRO

You were angry and manly to shatter the sleep of your
    throat;
The kiss of your blast is upon me, O friend of my fear,
And I savour your breath like a perfume as salt and
    austere
As the scent of the thunder of heaven that brims in the
    moat!

I grip you. We lie on the ground in the thongs of our
    clasp
And we stare like the hunter who starts at a tenuous
    cry;
We have wounded the wind with a wire and stung in
    the sky
A white hole that is small and unseen as the bite of the
    asp.

The smooth of your cheek—Do you sight from the
    depth of your eye
More faultless than vision, more true than the aiming
    of stars?
Is the heart of your hatred the target of redness of
    Mars

Or the roundness of heart of the one who must stumble
    and die?

O the valley is silent and shocked. I absolve from your
    name
The exaction of murder, my gun. It is I who have
    killed.
It is I whose enjoyment of horror is fine and fulfilled.
You are only the toy of my terror, my emblem of blame.

Come with me. We shall creep for his eyes like the
    sweat of my skin,
For the wind is repaired and the fallen is calling for
    breath.
You are only the means of the practical humor of
    death
Which is savage to punish the dead for the sake of
    my sin!

1945

PROCONSUL

JOHN DOS PASSOS

In the unmilitary United States there flourished during the nineteenth century a number of families who raised their children to the sound of bugles; among the most dashing were the MacArthurs.

The first general, Arthur MacArthur, was the son of a Scottish lawyer who had become City Attorney in Milwaukee and Lieutenant Governor of the state. At seventeen he joined the 24th Wisconsin Regiment to help quench the rebellion. He carried the regimental colors through the smoke and slaughter of Missionary Ridge and became known as "the Boy Colonel of the West." He continued in the army after Appomattox, married the daughter of a North Carolina physician and went to fight Indians. It was a life of jingling spurs and sweated saddles and trailbreaking;

reveille and taps on the parade grounds of dusty outposts.

On January 26 1880 at the Little Rock Barracks there was born to the MacArthurs a son who was to fulfill their fondest hopes. "I think there is material for a soldier in the boy," said the father when he took young Douglas, wearing a mass of golden curls and bearing a toy musket over his shoulder, to be photographed in San Antonio. While his father was stationed at Fort Sam Houston, young Douglas attended the West Texas Military Academy. There he won a gold medal for "extraordinary excellence" in sports, deportment and scholarship.

While the son was astonishing the schoolmasters the father was earning a Congressional Medal and climbing promotion's ladder to Lieutenant General (American generals were scarce in those days) and Chief of Staff.

When the short summer war against Spain almost by accident catapulted the American dream into the sweltering Orient the elder MacArthur received the assignment of straightening out the Filipinos. The Insurrectos had been all for American help to throw out the Spaniards, but when the Americans decided to stay they turned recalcitrant. The five year pacification proved an ugly business.

> Underneath the starry flag
> Civilize them with a Krag

went the soldier's song. (There was more to it than that: with the rifle and the flag went the old copybook maxims; life, liberty and the pursuit of happiness; devoted missionaries and teachers, effective administrators and the new science of sanitation. For better or worse after Aguinaldo's surrender the conglomerate populations of those distant scattered islands began to

see their future as American.) Arthur MacArthur was
our first proconsul.

He looked the part. He acted the part. His arbitrary
behavior caused misgivings among the Washington civilians. When a civilian commissioner arrived to in-
stall due process he was treated with scant respect. In
1901 General Arthur MacArthur was summarily relieved of his command.

Meanwhile young Douglas, with his mother in
Milwaukee, was tutoring for the West Point exami-
nations. A brother was already at Annapolis. Needless
to say Douglas MacArthur passed with an extraordinary score. A tall handsome deadly serious young man
with impeccable manners, in spite of a little rougher
than the usual hazing by upperclassmen, in spite of
the indefatigable supervision of an ubiquitous mother
who insisted on renting a house near the Military
Academy to be near him, he broke all records of
scholastic and military deportment. He made the base-
ball team. As senior he was First Captain. He graduated at the top of his class.

He chose the unpopular Corps of Engineers because
advancement was rapidest there.

He saw his first field service in the Philippines but
soon he was detailed to Tokyo as his father's aide on a
spit and polish mission to the Orient. He accompanied
General Arthur MacArthur as an observer during the
Russo-Japanese War.

When in 1912 the father died suddenly of a heart
attack at a Grand Army reunion of his old Wisconsin

regiment the son was already well on his way to succeed him. He held various staff jobs in Washington.
When Woodrow Wilson began to apply the Big Stick
to the tumultuous Mexicans, the youthful Captain
MacArthur in the company of a young German observer named Fritz von Papen scouted hostile positions outside of Vera Cruz, disguised, his biographers
tell us, as "a Mexican bum."

World War I found him in France as chief of General Menoker's staff. It was MacArthur's idea to assem-
ble a Rainbow Division made up from units of twenty-
seven different state militias. He believed in the citi-
zen soldier.

Preux chevalier sans peur et sans reproche, already
he had a reputation for never perspiring. His uniform
didn't wilt in the hottest weather. He seemed without
fear. He went into combat without sidearms or gas-
mask or helmet. He'd taken to pulling the wire lining
out of the stiff uniform cap and wearing it at a rakish
angle. Newspapermen called him d'Artagnan of the
AEF.

He won his promotion to colonel on the battlefield. He was gassed, twice wounded, decorated thir-
teen times, cited seven times for extreme bravery under
fire. Pershing promoted him to Brigadier General and
put him in command of the Rainbow Division he had
helped create.

After the war he was for three years Superintendent
at West Point. It was MacArthur who first gave the
cadets a complete college curriculum and introduced
compulsory athletics. Of course he was the youngest

superintendent on record, as he'd been the youngest
brigadier general, and the youngest divisional commander.

He married late (assuredly the dowager Mrs. Mac-
Arthur had kept the girls at bay); even then it seemed
more an affair of the Social Register than of the heart.
Louise Cromwell Brooks was a rich grass widow who
had queened it over the social doings of the higher
echelons of the AEF in Paris after the armistice. General Pershing, himself a widower, is said to have suffered from her charms. The society columns hailed the
affair as *The Marriage of Mars and Millions*.

The union was shortlived. After the splendors of
New York and Paris the lady is said to have found
Manila, where MacArthur was appointed to his father's
old post as American commander, quite unamusing.
It is admitted that the general lacked humor.

These were trying years. When General Mac-
Arthur became Chief of Staff in 1930 the army was
unpopular. Disarmament was the obsession. Because
MacArthur saw dangers ahead from the rising dictatorships of Germany and Japan he was labeled a war-
monger. His trips abroad were described as medal
hunts.

MacArthur had a bad press.

When President Hoover ordered him to disperse the
bonus marchers the Communists were stirring up to
sedition in their poor Hooverville on Anacostia Flats,
he superintended the job—which he could well have
foisted off on a subordinate—himself, and saw that it

was done efficiently and with a minimum of bloodlet-
ting. For that public service he was denounced as a
"man on a white horse" by the weteyed journalists
who were heralding the New Deal revolution.

It was noised against him that seven years before
he'd sat on the courtmartial that dismissed his friend
Billy Mitchell from the service for expressing too soon
his conviction of the wartime ascendancy of the air-
plane. The vote was secret. Not till years later did the
story leak out that MacArthur had voted for acquittal.

All the same Franklin Roosevelt put through his ap-
pointment as Chief of Staff for an unheard-of second
term. What little combat readiness there was in the
army the day of Pearl Harbor was largely due to Mac-
Arthur's interest in motorized warfare.

In 1935 Manuel Quezon, who as a boy Insurrecto
had surrendered to MacArthur's father, became the
President of the independent Philippine Commonwealth. Alarmed by the advance of the Japanese Co-
prosperity Sphere, he asked Washington for the loan
of the American general best versed in Far Eastern
affairs to help plan the islands' defense.

At the age of fiftyseven Douglas MacArthur retired
from the United States Army to become Field Marshal
in the Army of the Philippines.

In the course of the long steamship trips between
the West coast and Manila he met, besieged and soon
married an agreeable young woman from Tennessee.

This time it was for keeps. The dowager Mrs. Mac-
Arthur, now a very old lady indomitably bent on fol-

lowing her son's career, reached Manila only in time
to take to her bed and die.

The MacArthurs were raising their small son at their
penthouse on the roof of the Manila Hotel when they
had news of Pearl Harbor.

MacArthur had been twentythree years a general
officer. According to the hymenopterous punctilio of
military stratification the general officer lives in a sealed
world. A proper brass hat doesn't know whether it's
raining or sunshine until he's briefed by his staff. Like
the queen bee he's fed on royal jelly.

MacArthur in the Philippines was the brass hat of
brass hats. A man of brilliant intelligence with the
real strategic bent, he must have been strangely cut
off from the real world to allow his Flying Fortresses,
after eight hours' warning, to be smashed in rows on
Clark Field by Japanese planes flying all the way
from Formosa. He hadn't enough planes or PT boats
to begin with. Now he had nothing.

He declared Manila an open city to save the lives
of the puzzled Filipinos who had trusted him as they
would trust the Virgin Mary.

The retreat to Bataan was a routine performance
plotted long ahead. It certainly was not lack of physical courage that kept him so long in the tunnel under
Corregidor. The doomed troops never saw hide or
hair of him. "Dugout Doug" they shouted after him
when he fled (under direct orders from Washington)
by PT boat, through infested seas to Mindanao. He
took his wife and the little boy and the little boy's
Chinese nurse along with him. There was just time to

snatch them in a fourmotor plane off the Del Monte strip before the Japs closed in.

It was the old MacArthur who stepped out of the plane on his first Australian airstrip. The American collapse, Rommel in Africa, the loss of the British battleships off Singapore had scared the Australians out of a year's growth. Their military men were talking grimly of holding the Brisbane line. MacArthur showed no interest at all in the Brisbane line. He talked of invading the Philippines. He would only plan for victory.

Fresh from humiliations and defeats that would have ruined any lesser general's career, the Aussies saw MacArthur sit cool and unwilted in his headquarters in Brisbane smoking his corncob pipe—a folksy touch that gave an edge to his starched uniform and punctilious manner—plotting the strategy of victory. "I came through and I shall return," he broadcast to the Filipinos to let them know he'd escaped through the Japanese lines. The Aussies caught fire from MacArthur.

He couldn't have done it without the navy, or the marines who squandered their lives on forgotten reefs and coralstrewn beaches. He couldn't have done it without the Aussie prospectors' early knowledge of the Owen Stanley Mountains and the stinking Kokoda trail in New Guinea; or without the amphibian techniques developed in the Central Pacific or the erosion of the Japanese airforce or the floating bases and the incredible supplylines that girdled the globe;

but he knew how to seize the right moment,

he knew that attack was defense;

with a chessplayer's skill he kept four moves ahead of the Japs; where they were he wasn't. Where their defense was spread thin he was landing in force;

until, leaving wellarmed Japanese troops frustrate and starving on a score of islands,

MacArthur, having darkened the sky over the Philippines with little books of matches bearing his picture "Rely on me: I shall return,"

waded nonchalantly ashore

amid the whirring of motion picture cameras

on Lingayen Beach.

"I have returned. Rally to me. Let no heart be faint."

"Boldness and disdain of the enemy" he explained to the correspondents at his headquarters at San Miguel the day his troops got their first toehold in the suburbs of Manila. He was proclaiming the city's capture...

(Press releases. Army and Navy and Marines; their brass fought the Japs allright, but they fought each other for headlines in the stateside press. MacArthur's PRO beat everything. God and the General were so often linked in the news people could hardly tell which was which.)

... there was mighty little left of Manila when after weeks of block by block fighting the last Jap threw up his hands. "Boldness and disdain of the enemy":

The Manhattan Project. Iwo Jima. Okinawa. The mushroomshaped cloud over cities become heaps. In spite of pulling and hauling in Washington by adher-

ents of the various services it was to MacArthur that
Harry Truman awarded the palm of victory. As Gen-
eral of the Army he took the Japanese surrender in
Tokyo Bay.

*   *   *

Supreme Ruler of Japan,
Douglas MacArthur was as inaccessible as he'd been
in that desperate tunnel under Corregidor, but somehow he managed, decking them out in terms of the
hour, to promulgate the old copybook maxims that had
Americanized the Filipinos in his father's time:
civil liberties,
    freedom of the press,
        land ownership for the peasants who worked
the soil, unhampered trade unions, the rules of fair
play. He kept the Communists off base and foiled the
best spy-diplomats that Moscow could train.

When the Emperor Hirohito renounced his divinity,
the displaced godhead seemed to hover for a while
over the GHQ of the Supreme Commander, Allied
Powers; Commander-in-Chief, United Nations Command; Commander-in-Chief, Far East; and Commanding General U.S. Army, Far East.

A movement to nominate him for the Presidency
in 1948 seemed an anticlimax. No American before
him had ever occupied such a pinnacle of power.

In spite of the five stars and the gold braided caps
and the chest banded with rainbow after rainbow of
ribbons

Douglas MacArthur, as an old man at seventyone, was to look once more

into the grinning skull of defeat.

When through a series of wrong moves, so maladroit that historians will be puzzling over them for a hundred years, the managers of America's destiny managed to leave the friendly republic they'd been fostering south of the 38th parallel in Korea

wide open to attack by the vigorous army the Russians trained in the north,

war broke out overnight.

Again as in Manila, it was MacArthur the unready. (All the brass hat knows is his briefing from his staff.) Early reverses were wiped out by a skillful amphibious landing at Inchon. MacArthur ordered the advance to the Yalu. In spite of the fact that the first Chinese thrust had been with difficulty repulsed, MacArthur's PRO's were filling the press with accounts of his troops eating Thanksgiving Dinner, victorious,

in sight of the Yalu River.

The mighty MacArthur would clear the peninsula and get the boys home by Christmas. A few days later the boys were on the run, or dead, or prisoners dripping with dysentery in stinking stockades.

"Boldness and disdain of the enemy." Every reader of the *New York Times* knew that the Chinese were massing an army on the Yalu; they announced it themselves. (A brass hat lives like a queen bee, sealed off from the world, dependent on his staff to feed him the royal jelly.)

In spite of the retreat conducted in the best War College style by the troops in the northern mountains (flying boxcars flew in a whole suspensionbridge for a rivercrossing by the First Marine Division)

the Chinese inflicted a smashing defeat

on the forces under MacArthur's command.

The rest was the facesaving diplomacy of failure.

When Douglas MacArthur was, like his father before him, summarily relieved of his proconsular post, the little wardheeler from Independence Missouri who occupied the White House

made the dismissal as curt he could,

but somehow he managed to give the impression that the general's crime had not been his defeat

but his insistence on planning to win;

"There is no substitute for victory."

Win or lose MacArthur had grandeur. Perhaps most Americans agreed with Harry Truman that grandeur was for the birds,

all the same they greeted him as no defeated general has ever been greeted before. In New York City the streetcleaners figured that sixteen million tons of paper and ticker tape were dumped out of office windows by the frenzied inhabitants during the MacArthur parade. Clearly a record. In Washington the members of both houses of Congress listened in awe

as the old general offered his ritual submission to

the civil government, and pulled about him the nostalgic toga of the old soldiers of the Republic (Washington too made his farewell):

"I am closing my fifty-two years of military service. When I joined the army, even before the turn of the century it was the fulfilment of all my boyish hopes and dreams ...

"... The world has turned over many times since I took the oath on the plain at West Point and the hopes and dreams have long since vanished ... 'Old soldiers never die, they just fade away.'"

He set the whole nation to humming the old song.

1961

TO THE FINISH:
A LETTER FROM IWO JIMA

EDGAR L. JONES

Our empty transport vessel with its deck-load of beaten-up landing craft is rolling heavily on the long voyage home from Iwo Jima. To provide quarters for casualties, the sick bay has been expanded until half the bunks, built in tiers of four, are now occupied by the wounded remnants of the Fourth Marines who rode the ship into battle.

The doctors aboard this particular ship are specialists in eye surgery and mental cases, so that in bed after bed one passes men who have lost their eyesight or their sanity. The same small boats which headed valiantly for the beach on D Day returned again and again on succeeding days with litter-loads of pain-crazed bodies; not really men, just bodies, which were salted down as the heavy seas broke over the bows of the lurching landing craft, jarred into sickening consciousness as the waves hurled the boats against the high walls of the transport, and finally lifted, two stretchers to a crane-load, onto the flat, steady decks of the ship which was to take them home.

Some of the more fortunate ones died during the night, and in the morning bodies, so tightly wrapped in gray blankets that they seemed pygmy size, were lined up on deck, waiting for the same small boats to take them ashore for burial. Among the less fortunate are one man who is faceless from the end of his nose to his hairline, and another whose right side is paralyzed, whose left arm is gone, and whose one remaining eye stares out of a pulpy mass of flesh. The doctors, who with such skill and untiring attention have kept these bodies alive, come into the wardroom, remove their rubber gloves and face masks, and sit over their coffee in brooding silence.

The brig contains the only Japanese prisoners, nine of them, to be captured prior to our departure on D plus ten. There were two others, but they died aboard ship, and two of the remaining are unconscious most of the time. The same small boats which took the first waves of Marines ashore and brought the endless waves of wounded back again also transported to the safety of the ship's brig those of the enemy who still had a breath of life.

In many ways the crews of those small boats were the heroes of the battle of Iwo Jima, because, tough as the Japanese were, the heavy seas were tougher. The prevailing winds reversed themselves during the first ten days, so that instead of being on the leeward side of the island, the beachhead was exposed to the sullen fury of the Pacific Ocean. Because Iwo Jima is a volcano rising straight out of the sea, there is no shallow water. The box-shaped landing craft were tossed about like egg crates caught on the crest of a spring flood. Unprotected by breakwaters or coral reefs, the boats were swamped by six-foot breakers as soon as their bows rammed into the volcanic sand. The boats floundered, sank, and were spewn along the shore to form twisted barricades of debris.

Despite their losses, the boat crews continued to shuttle men and materials. The men rarely slept, and depended for food upon having someone aboard a transport pass down K rations and an occasional sandwich. The crew of one small boat from this ship, manned like so many others by Coast Guard personnel, went four days and nights without relief. The men could barely walk when they finally came aboard to sleep.

The waves hit the beach at an angle, swinging the boats sidewise and overturning them before the ramps could be let down. The Marine beach parties and Seabees had to resort to bulldozers and stern lines to keep the craft at right angles to the shore long enough to roll the matériel onto the sand. While a bulldozer with a tow chain kept the ramp anchored in the sand, a small tug with a stout line on the stern strained against the current to prevent the landing craft from being swept broadside against the shoreline. As the men rushed to unload vehicles, ammunition, and food, the breakers swarmed over the sterns of the landing craft, swamping some and leaving the rest half filled with water. The crews were never dry.

As if the seas were not enough to contend with, the Japanese had the entire beach under mortar and shell fire, so that the men never knew when a shell would explode in their midst. Our transport was lying close offshore, enabling the correspondents to go onto the beach each morning and return at night to such luxuries as a hot shower, warm meals, and a dry bed.

Even when we reached the beach on the morning of the seventh day, a flurry of mortar shells hit the landing craft to our left and right. We were free to scramble through the deep sand to the nearest hole, but the crew of the boat was left to manhandle the cargo with no more protection than a steel helmet.

Each of the half-dozen beaches had a beachmaster who stood on high ground with a microphone and directed unloading operations. A powerful battery of loudspeakers carried his commands to landing craft waiting to come in, to bulldozer crews, and to Marine working parties. Though shells burst around him, the beachmaster stood his ground and with a caustic voice of assurance kept the traffic moving with invectives interlarded with: "You there in boat number 457, whatja got 'board? All right, ride in on the next breaker. Hey, you cat drivers, get the hell down here with your tails in the water. Clear that truck out of there. You Marines start moving or we'll bury you under. Drop the hawser! *Drop the hawser!* Swing her starboard." And so on.

Working with the beachmasters were the floating traffic cops, the men in control boats who remained a few hundred yards offshore and regulated the successive waves of landing craft. Beyond them were the destroyers, blasting away with their five-inch guns whenever the Marines struck an enemy strong point; and still farther out, riding at anchor, were the transports, tankers, LCT's, cargo vessels, and floating drydocks. On the horizon one could see the small, fast ships in the antisubmarine patrol, and somewhere out of sight were the aircraft carriers which sent forth fighters and fighter bombers whenever enemy tanks or pillboxes were discovered. The larger units of the fleet, the battleships and cruisers, stood by, after having finished their three-day bombardment prior to the invasion, and fired their heavy guns only when a specific target required a salvo of eight- or sixteen-inch shells for permanent liquidation.

Two years ago, and possibly even one year ago, American forces would have lost the battle of Iwo Jima. The island was more heavily fortified than any previous one captured. The knee-deep volcanic sand stopped all vehicles in their tracks, and the heavy seas littered the two-mile beach with the shredded remains of boats, tanks, half-tracks, amphibious trucks, and jeeps. Yet the bulldozers were brought ashore to open lanes through the deep sand. Steel tracks were laid to enable tanks and trucks to reach more solid terrain; cranes were set up along the beach; heavy artillery was hauled ashore, along with steam rollers, road graders, and prime movers. The entire operation followed a tested pattern which neither the Japs nor the weather could stop.

American tacticians had learned much between Tarawa and Iwo Jima about island-to-island fighting, but so had the Japanese. The landing followed a pattern which in three years has become a tradition: a long period of bombing from the air, a shorter flurry of concentrated naval gunfire, a final assault at close range which utilized every type of weapon that floats or flies, and then the Marines landed. The Japanese knew what to expect, and had planned accordingly. The bombings they could not stop, so they went under-

ground where the bombs could not reach them. The
rocky cliffs of Iwo were so soft that a man with a pick
and shovel could dig himself a comfortable cave in a
day.

For sixty-eight consecutive days the Army bombed
Iwo. The Japanese lost all their planes and most of
their surface installations, but they and their guns
survived. On the sixty-ninth day, at dawn, the American Navy began its bombardment; the Japanese remained in hiding during the three days that the Navy
poured a record tonnage of explosives on the island.
They could not stop the Fleet any more than they
could the Army bombers, so they did not try.

Their defense was based on not giving away their positions or revealing their strength until an actual landing was attempted. They had only a handful of coastal
batteries; and the only time I saw one of them in action, it hit a ship. The Japanese policy was not to fire
unless they were sure they could not miss. They allowed endless waves of carrier planes to make their
bombing runs unmolested, but they practically threw
the island at observation planes which served as the
eyes of the Fleet.

Their defense plan was a simple one; they dug their
guns into the high ground in such a way that they had
the beaches in a cross fire. Because they did not intend
to fire back at the Fleet, it was unnecessary to have
their guns facing the sea. The advantages of such a
plan are obvious. They could mount their guns in reinforced caves which had only small openings facing
inland. The Fleet could have circled the island for
weeks and still not have been able to bring direct fire

to bear on the entrances of the caves. The guns dug into Mount Suribachi pointed to the north, while those in the cliffs overlooking the northern end of the beach faced to the south. The Fleet was firing from the east and west.

Had the Navy known the exact location of the caves, they might have had some success in firing over Suribachi into the cliffs on the northern part of the island, and vice versa; the Japanese, however, shrewdly avoided revealing their positions. They had the beach completely covered, and the beach was all they were interested in.

I go into this at length to counteract any notion that the Fleet did not give adequate support to the landing parties. For three days prior to D Day I was on a light cruiser. No fleet ever moved in closer and unloaded so many high explosives on so small a stretch of land. For two of those three days a heavy mist obscured the island, so that even the observation planes hovering overhead could not tell with certainty where the shells were landing or how much damage they were doing. The Japanese camouflaged the entrances of their caves. Once the camouflage was torn away, succeeding salvos found their mark. In other places, however, the caves had armor-plated doors as protection, and luck was as essential as accuracy in knocking them out. The entire faces of hills tumbled down, but it was still anyone's guess whether the right caves had been sealed off in the process.

In walking around Iwo later, I saw cement block-houses which the Navy had pulverized into pieces so small that I could have picked up and carried away what was left as a souvenir. The face of Suribachi had been pushed back fifteen feet. Remains of some Japanese showed the effect of eight- and sixteen-inch shells exploding at close range, and there were others dead without a scratch on them. The heads were grotesquely misshapen by concussion, however, just as though someone had taken a ball of putty and squeezed it. When the Navy had a definite target to aim at, it left no doubt of its firepower.

Whether Iwo will have any lasting military significance is something which men out here argue about. In the midst of mobile warfare, Iwo nearly proved that a stationary defense was invulnerable, but there were too many flukes working against the invaders to make any generalization possible. Probably the most significant thing about the battle for Iwo was its inevitableness. No American operation was less secret. Everyone in the Pacific, including the Japanese, knew that the island had to be taken, knew approximately when it would be taken, and how it would be taken. This does not imply faulty security. It simply means that Iwo was next on the list of steppingstones to Tokyo, and there was only one way to capture it.

The island could not be knocked out from the air or sea. It had to be stormed when the typhoon season had passed, and when the prevailing winds were such that the eastern beaches were on the leeward side of the island. The master stroke of American strategy was having a task force at large between Iwo and Japan. This left the Japanese on Iwo without air or naval support.

The Japanese, under the command of an artillery

officer, fought a smarter battle with better weapons than in any previous engagement. With an abrupt change of tactics, they fought with the skill of the German Army. Yet 20,000 Japanese did not stop 40,000 Marines from landing in small boats from the open sea. Any evaluation of opposing tactics must, I suppose, be based on which side won, unless future historians prove that the Japanese made the United States pay more for Iwo than the island was worth.

The first time I went onto the beach was D Day plus four. I went in with a large group of Fourth Division Marines. The beach was another Anzio. The Japanese were lobbing shells into supply dumps, ammunition depots, communication centers, and every other place where they saw men or machinery concentrated. No man on the beach felt secure. The Americans held about one square mile of low ground at that point, most of which I toured. Everywhere men were struggling: to keep landing craft from submerging, to dig roads in the deep sand, to push mired trucks onto solid ground, to haul equipment to sheltered locations, and to fight nature for the chance to get on with the battle. And all the time the Japanese shells whined down and tore into sand and flesh with indiscriminate fury.

Trying as the volcanic sand of Iwo proved to be, it was also a blessing. The Japanese shells buried themselves, and the sand absorbed most of the shrapnel. Usually a man was killed instantly by having a shell land beside him in the foxhole, or he escaped without injury. This did not hold true when a shell landed in a boat, or when one dropped in the midst of a beach party. What impressed me most, however, was the absence of dead Japanese. Some had been buried, of course, and others had died underground, but it was unnatural to find so few bodies after so much fighting. There were American bodies—more than 3000 of them buried or not yet buried—but where were the Japanese? Everyone I questioned simply pointed to the hills on the left and right and swore fervently.

Iwo was unlike any war I had ever seen. It was a fight to the finish, with no man asking for quarter until he was dead. Of the nearly 20,000 American casualties, approximately two thirds were wounded, but all except a few score of the 20,000 Japanese died where they fell. There is such a thing as dying decently, but not on Iwo. I do not believe anything practical can be achieved by describing men blown apart. Veterans of two and three years of war in the Pacific were sickened. An estimated 26,000 men died in eight square miles of fighting.

I returned to Iwo on D Day plus six, seven, and eight. By that time the Marines had captured territory where Japanese had lain dead in the hot sun for more than a week. I crawled into pillboxes burned out by flame throwers, and into deep caves where the Japanese had been burning their own dead to conceal the extent of their losses. I was torturing myself to look at the results of war, because I think it is essential for civilians occasionally to hold their noses and see what is going on.

The sight on Iwo which I could not force myself to see again was the section of the beach allotted for an American cemetery. The chaplains were endeavoring to identify each body and hold a brief, individual service for each man to be buried in the black sands of the barren island. Naturally the chaplains and the burial parties were far behind in their work. The dead were brought in faster than they could be buried.

On the afternoon I walked by, there was half an acre of dead Marines stretched out so close together that they blanketed the beach for two hundred yards. The stench was overpowering. There, in mangled lots, not laid in neat rows, was part of the price paid for Iwo. All I could think of as I hurried by was the old priest who died in Dostoevski's *The Brothers Karamazov* and shocked his followers by decomposing before the burial service. The smell of one's countrymen rotting in the sun is a lasting impression.

Perhaps one becomes accustomed to it. To me it was an experience which made it impossible for me to return to Iwo. Undoubtedly I shirked my duty, but I never could have been an impartial observer after that. I cannot evaluate the battle for Iwo objectively. The Marines fought with courage and determination seemingly beyond human capabilities. They died the hard way.

1945

PART THREE

THE EFFECTS OF WAR

TO THE MEMORY OF THE BRAVE AMERICANS

Under General Greene,
in South Carolina, who Fell
in the Action of September 8, 1781

PHILIP FRENEAU

At Eutaw Springs the valiant died;
  Their limbs with dust are covered o'er—
Weep on, ye springs, your tearful tide;
  How many heroes are no more!

If in this wreck of ruin, they
  Can yet be thought to claim a tear,
O smite your gentle breast, and say
  The friends of freedom slumber here!

Thou, who shalt trace this bloody plain,
  If goodness rules thy generous breast,
Sigh for the wasted rural reign;
  Sigh for the shepherds, sunk to rest!

Stranger, their humble graves adorn;
  You too may fall, and ask a tear;
'Tis not the beauty of the morn
  That proves the evening shall be clear.—

They saw their injured country's woe;
  The flaming town, the wasted field;
Then rushed to meet the insulting foe;
  They took the spear—but left the shield.

Led by thy conquering genius, Greene,
  The Britons they compelled to fly;
None distant viewed the fatal plain,
  None grieved, in such a cause to die—

But, like the Parthian, famed of old,
  Who, flying, still their arrows threw,
These routed Britons, full as bold,
  Retreated, and retreating slew.

Now rest in peace, our patriot band;
  Though far from nature's limits thrown,
We trust they find a happier land,
  A brighter sunshine of their own.

1781

THE ARSENAL
AT SPRINGFIELD

HENRY WADSWORTH LONGFELLOW

This is the Arsenal. From floor to ceiling,
  Like a huge organ, rise the burnished arms;
But from their silent pipes no anthem pealing
  Startles the villages with strange alarms.

Ah! what a sound will rise, how wild and dreary,
  When the death-angel touches those swift keys!
What loud lament and dismal Miserere
  Will mingle with their awful symphonies!

I hear even now the infinite fierce chorus,
  The cries of agony, the endless groan,
Which, through the ages that have gone before us,
  In long reverberations reach our own.

On helm and harness rings the Saxon hammer,
  Through Cimbric forest roars the Norseman's song,
And loud, amid the universal clamor,
  O'er distant deserts sounds the Tartar gong.

I hear the Florentine, who from his palace
  Wheels out his battle-bell with dreadful din,

And Aztec priests upon their teocallis
  Beat the wild war-drums made of serpent's skin;

The tumult of each sacked and burning village;
  The shout that every prayer for mercy drowns;
The soldiers' revels in the midst of pillage;
  The wail of famine in beleaguered towns;

The bursting shell, the gateway wrenched asunder,
  The rattling musketry, the clashing blade;
And ever and anon, in tones of thunder,
  The diapason of the cannonade.

Is it, O man, with such discordant noises,
  With such accursed instruments as these,
Thou drownest Nature's sweet and kindly voices,
  And jarrest the celestial harmonies?

Were half the power that fills the world with terror,
  Were half the wealth bestowed on camps and courts,
Given to redeem the human mind from error,
  There were no need of arsenals or forts:

The warrior's name would be a name abhorrèd!
  And every nation, that should lift again
Its hand against a brother, on its forehead
  Would wear forevermore the curse of Cain!

Down the dark future, through long generations,
  The echoing sounds grow fainter and then cease;
And like a bell, with solemn, sweet vibrations,
  I hear once more the voice of Christ say, "Peace!"

Peace! and no longer from its brazen portals
   The blast of War's great organ shakes the skies!
But beautiful as songs of the immortals,
   The holy melodies of love arise.

1844

MALVERN HILL

HERMAN MELVILLE

Ye elms that wave on Malvern Hill
   In prime of morn and May,
Recall ye how McClellan's men
    Here stood at bay?
While deep within yon forest dim
   Our rigid comrades lay—
Some with the cartridge in their mouth,
Others with fixed arms lifted South—
     Invoking so
The cypress glades? Ah wilds of woe!

The spires of Richmond, late beheld
   Through rifts in musket-haze,
Were closed from view in clouds of dust
    On leaf-walled ways,
Where streamed our wagons in caravan;
   And the Seven Nights and Days
Of march and fast, retreat and fight,
Pinched our grimed faces to ghastly plight—
    Does the elm wood
Recall the haggard beards of blood?

The battle-smoked flag, with stars eclipsed,
   We followed (it never fell!)—
In silence husbanded our strength—
   Received their yell;
Till on this slope we patient turned
With cannon ordered well;
Reverse we proved was not defeat;
But ah, the sod what thousands meet!—
   Does Malvern Wood
Bethink itself, and muse and brood?

   We elms of Malvern Hill
     Remember everything;
   But sap the twig will fill:
   Wag the world how it will,
     Leaves must be green in Spring.

1866

ABRAHAM LINCOLN'S GETTYSBURG ADDRESS

Four score and seven years ago our fathers brought forth on this continent, a new nation, conceived in Liberty, and dedicated to the proposition that all men are created equal.

Now we are engaged in a great civil war; testing whether that nation, or any nation so conceived and so dedicated, can long endure. We are met on a great battlefield of that war. We have come to dedicate a portion of that field as a final resting-place for those who here gave their lives that that nation might live. It is altogether fitting and proper that we should do this.

But, in a larger sense, we cannot dedicate—we cannot consecrate—we cannot hallow—this ground. The brave men, living and dead, who struggled here have consecrated it, far above our poor power to add or detract. The world will little note, nor long remember, what we say here, but it can never forget what they did here. It is for us the living, rather, to be dedicated here to the unfinished work which they who fought here have thus far so nobly advanced. It is rather for us to be here dedicated to the great task remaining before us—that from these honored dead we take

increased devotion to that cause for which they gave
the last full measure of devotion; that we here highly
resolve that these dead shall not have died in vain;
that this nation, under God, shall have a new birth of
freedom; and that government of the people, by the
people, for the people, shall not perish from the earth.

1863

COME UP FROM THE FIELDS FATHER

WALT WHITMAN

Come up from the fields father, here's a letter from
    our Pete,
And come to the front door mother, here's a letter from
    thy dear son.

Lo, 'tis autumn,
Lo, where the trees, deeper green, yellower and redder,
Cool and sweeten Ohio's villages with leaves fluttering
    in the moderate wind,
Where apples ripe in the orchards hang and grapes on
    the trellis'd vines,
(Smell you the smell of the grapes on the vines?
Smell you the buckwheat where the bees were lately
    buzzing?)
Above all, lo, the sky so calm, so transparent after the
    rain, and with wondrous clouds,
Below too, all calm, all vital and beautiful, and the
    farm prospers well.

Down in the fields all prospers well,
But now from the fields come father, come at the
    daughter's call,

And come to the entry mother, to the front door come
    right away.

Fast as she can she hurries, something ominous, her
    steps trembling,
She does not tarry to smooth her hair nor adjust her
    cap.

Open the envelope quickly,
O this is not our son's writing, yet his name is sign'd,
O a strange hand writes for our dear son, O stricken
    mother's soul!

All swims before her eyes, flashes with black, she
    catches the main words only,
Sentences broken, *gunshot wound in the breast, cav-
alry skirmish, taken to hospital,*
At present low, but will soon be better.

Ah now the single figure to me,
Amid all teeming and wealthy Ohio with all its cities
    and farms,
Sickly white in the face and dull in the head, very
    faint,
By the jamb of a door leans.

Grieve not so, dear mother, (the just-grown daughter
    speaks through her sobs,
The little sisters huddle around speechless and dis-
    may'd,)
*See dearest mother, the letter says Pete will soon be
    better.*

Alas poor boy, he will never be better, (nor may-be
    needs to be better that brave and simple soul,)
While they stand at home at the door he is dead al-
    ready,
The only son is dead.

But the mother needs to be better,
She with thin form presently drest in black,
By day her meals untouch'd, then at night fitfully
    sleeping, often waking,
In the midnight waking, weeping, longing with one
    deep longing,
O that she might withdraw unnoticed, silent from
    life escape and withdraw,
To follow, to seek, to be with her dear dead son.

1865

THE RETURN
OF A PRIVATE

HAMLIN GARLAND

The nearer the train drew toward La Crosse, the soberer the little group of "vets" became. On the long way from New Orleans they had beguiled tedium with jokes and friendly chaff; or with planning with elaborate detail what they were going to do now, after the war. A long journey, slowly, irregularly, yet persistently pushing northward. When they entered on Wisconsin territory they gave a cheer, and another when they reached Madison, but after that they sank into a dumb expectancy. Comrades dropped off at one or two points beyond, until there were only four or five left who were bound for La Crosse County.

Three of them were gaunt and brown, the fourth was gaunt and pale, with signs of fever and ague upon him. One had a great scar down his temple, one limped, and they all had unnaturally large, bright eyes, showing emaciation. There were no bands greeting them at the station, no banks of gayly-dressed ladies waving handkerchiefs and shouting "Bravo!" as they came in on the caboose of a freight train into the towns that had cheered and blared at them on their way to war. As they looked out or stepped upon the platform for a moment, as the train stood at the station, the loafers looked at them indifferently. Their blue coats, dusty and grimy, were too familiar now to excite notice, much less a friendly word. They were the last of the army to return, and the loafers were surfeited with such sights.

The train jogged forward so slowly that it seemed likely to be midnight before they should reach La Crosse. The little squad grumbled and swore, but it was no use; the train would not hurry, and, as a matter of fact, it was nearly two o'clock when the engine whistled "down brakes."

All of the group were farmers, living in districts several miles out of the town, and all were poor.

"Now, boys," said Private Smith, he of the fever and ague, "we are landed in La Crosse in the night. We've got to stay somewhere till mornin'. Now I ain't got no two dollars to waste on a hotel. I've got a wife and children, so I'm goin' to roost on a bench and take the cost of a bed out of my hide."

"Same here," put in one of the other men. "Hide 'll grow on again, dollars 'll come hard. It's goin' to be mighty hot skirmishin' to find a dollar these days."

"Don't think they'll be a deputation of citizens waitin' to 'scort us to a hotel, eh?" said another. His sarcasm was too obvious to require an answer.

Smith went on: "Then at daybreak we'll start for home—at least, I will."

"Well, I'll be dummed if I'll take two dollars out o' *my* hide," one of the younger men said. "I'm goin' to a hotel, ef I don't never lay up a cent."

"That'll do f'r you," said Smith; "but if you had a wife an' three young uns dependin' on yeh—"

"Which I ain't, thank the Lord! and don't intend havin' while the court knows itself."

The station was deserted, chill, and dark, as they came into it at exactly a quarter to two in the morning. Lit by the oil lamps that flared a dull red light over the dingy benches, the waiting-room was not an inviting place. The younger man went off to look up a hotel, while the rest remained and prepared to camp down on the floor and benches. Smith was attended to tenderly by the other men, who spread their blankets on the bench for him, and, by robbing themselves, made quite a comfortable bed, though the narrowness of the bench made his sleeping precarious.

It was chill, though August, and the two men, sitting with bowed heads, grew stiff with cold and weariness, and were forced to rise now and again and walk about to warm their stiffened limbs. It did not occur to them, probably, to contrast their coming home with their going forth, or with the coming home of the generals, colonels, or even captains—but to Private Smith, at any rate, there came a sickness at heart almost deadly as he lay there on his hard bed and went over his situation.

In the deep of the night, lying on a board in the town where he had enlisted three years ago, all elation and enthusiasm gone out of him, he faced the fact that with the joy of home-coming was already mingled the bitter juice of care. He saw himself sick, worn out, taking up the work on his half-cleared farm, the inevitable mortgage standing ready with open jaw to swallow half his earnings. He had given three years of his life for a mere pittance of pay, and now!—

Morning dawned at last, slowly, with a pale yellow
dome of light rising silently above the bluffs, which
stand like some huge storm-devastated castle, just east
of the city. Out to the left the great river swept on its
massive yet silent way to the south. Bluejays called
across the river from hillside to hillside through the
clear, beautiful air, and hawks began to skim the tops
of the hills. The older men were astir early, but Private
Smith had fallen at last into a sleep, and they went out
without waking him. He lay on his knapsack, his gaunt
face turned toward the ceiling, his hands clasped on his
breast, with a curious pathetic effect of weakness and
appeal.

An engine switching near woke him at last, and he
slowly sat up and stared about. He looked out of the
window and saw that the sun was lightening the hills
across the river. He rose and brushed his hair as well as
he could, folded his blankets up, and went out to find
his companions. They stood gazing silently at the river
and at the hills.

"Looks natcher'l, don't it?" they said, as he came out.

"That's what it does," he replied. "An' it looks good.
D'yeh see that peak?" He pointed at a beautiful sym-
metrical peak, rising like a slightly truncated cone, so
high that it seemed the very highest of them all. It was
lighted by the morning sun till it glowed like a beacon,
and a light scarf of gray morning fog was rolling up its
shadowed side.

"My farm's just beyond that. Now, if I can only
ketch a ride, we'll be home by dinner-time."

"I'm talkin' about breakfast," said one of the others.

"I guess it's one more meal o' hardtack f'r me," said Smith.

They foraged around, and finally found a restaurant with a sleepy old German behind the counter, and procured some coffee, which they drank to wash down their hardtack.

"Time'll come," said Smith, holding up a piece by the corner, "when this'll be a curiosity."

"I hope to God it will! I bet I've chawed hardtack enough to shingle every house in the coolly. I've chawed it when my lampers was down, and when they wasn't. I've took it dry, soaked, and mashed. I've had it wormy, musty, sour, and blue mouldy. I've had it in little bits and big bits; 'fore coffee an' after coffee. I'm ready f'r a change. I'd like t' git holt jest about now o' some of the hot biscuits my wife c'n make when she lays herself out f'r company."

"Well, if you set there gabblin', you'll never *see* yer wife."

"Come on," said Private Smith. "Wait a moment, boys; less take suthin'. It's on me." He led them to the rusty tin dipper which hung on a nail beside the wooden water-pail, and they grinned and drank. Then shouldering their blankets and muskets, which they were "takin' home to the boys," they struck out on their last march.

"They called that coffee Jayvy," grumbled one of them, "but it never went by the road where government Jayvy resides. I reckon I know coffee from peas."

They kept together on the road along the turnpike, and up the winding road by the river, which they followed for some miles. The river was very lovely, curving down along its sandy beds, pausing now and then under broad basswood trees, or running in dark, swift, silent currents under tangles of wild grape-vines, and drooping alders, and haw trees. At one of these lovely spots the three vets sat down on the thick green sward to rest, "on Smith's account." The leaves of the trees were as fresh and green as in June, the jays called cheery greetings to them, and kingfishers darted to and fro with swooping, noiseless flight.

"I tell yeh, boys, this knocks the swamps of Loueesi-ana into kingdom come."

"You bet. All they c'n raise down there is snakes, niggers, and p'rticler hell."

"An' fightin' men," put in the older man.

"An' fightin' men. If I had a good hook an' line I'd sneak a pick'rel out o' that pond. Say, remember that time I shot that alligator—"

"I guess we'd better be crawlin' along," interrupted Smith, rising and shouldering his knapsack, with considerable effort, which he tried to hide.

"Say, Smith, lemme give you a lift on that."

"I guess I c'n manage," said Smith, grimly.

"Course. But, yo' see, I may not have a chance right off to pay yeh back for the times you've carried my gun and hull caboodle. Say, now, gimme that gun, anyway."

"All right, if yeh feel like it, Jim," Smith replied, and they trudged along doggedly in the sun, which was getting higher and hotter each half-mile.

"Ain't it queer there ain't no teams comin' along," said Smith after a long silence.

"Well, no, seein' 's it's Sunday."

"By jinks, that's a fact. It *is* Sunday. I'll git home in time f'r dinner, sure!" he exulted. "She don't hev dinner usually till about *one* on Sundays." And he fell into a muse, in which he smiled.

"Well, I'll git home jest about six o'clock, jest about when the boys are milkin' the cows," said old Jim Cranby. "I'll step into the barn, an' then I'll say: 'Heah! why ain't this milkin' done before this time o' day?' An' then won't they yell!" he added, slapping his thigh in great glee.

Smith went on. "I'll jest go up the path. Old Rover 'll come down the road to meet me. He won't bark; he'll know me, an' he'll come down waggin' his tail an' showin' his teeth. That's his way of laughin'. An' so I'll walk up to the kitchen door, an' I'll say, '*Dinner* f'r a hungry man!' An' then she'll jump up, an'—"

He couldn't go on. His voice choked at the thought of it. Saunders, the third man, hardly uttered a word. He walked silently behind the others. He had lost his wife the first year he was in the army. She died of pneumonia caught in the autumn rains, while working in the fields in his place.

They plodded along till at last they came to a parting of the ways. To the right the road continued up the main valley; to the left it went over the main ridge.

"Well, boys," began Smith, as they grounded their muskets and looked away up the valley, "here's where we shake hands. We've marched together a good many miles, an' now I s'pose we're done."

"Yes, I don't think we'll do any more of it f'r a while. I don' want to, I know."

"I hope I'll see yeh once in a while, boys, to talk over old times."

"Of course," said Saunders, whose voice trembled a little, too. "It ain't *exactly* like dyin'." They all found it hard to look at each other.

"But we'd ought'r go home with you," said Cranby. "You'll never climb that ridge with all them things on yer back."

"Oh, I'm all right! Don't worry about me. Every step takes me nearer home, yeh see. Well, good-by, boys."

They shook hands. "Good-by. Good luck!"

"Same to you. Lemme know how you find things at home."

"Good-by."

"Good-by."

He turned once before they passed out of sight, and waved his cap, and they did the same, and all yelled. Then all marched away with their long, steady, loping, veteran step. The solitary climber in blue walked on for a time, with his mind filled with the kindness of his comrades, and musing upon the many wonderful days they had had together in camp and field.

He thought of his chum, Billy Tripp. Poor Billy! A "minie" ball fell into his breast one day, fell wailing like a cat, and tore a great ragged hole in his heart. He looked forward to a sad scene with Billy's mother and sweetheart. They would want to know all about it. He tried to recall all that Billy had said, and the particulars of it, but there was little to remember, just that wild wailing sound high in the air, a dull slap, a short, quick, expulsive groan, and the boy lay with his face in the dirt in the ploughed field they were marching across.

That was all. But all the scenes he had since been through had not dimmed the horror, the terror of that moment, when his boy comrade fell, with only a breath between a laugh and a death-groan. Poor handsome Billy! Worth millions of dollars was his young life.

These sombre recollections gave way at length to more cheerful feelings as he began to approach his home coulé. The fields and houses grew familiar, and in one or two he was greeted by people seated in the doorway. But he was in no mood to talk, and pushed on steadily, though he stopped and accepted a drink of milk once at the well-side of a neighbor.

The sun was getting hot on that slope, and his step grew slower, in spite of his iron resolution. He sat down several times to rest. Slowly he crawled up the rough, reddish-brown road, which wound along the hillside, under great trees, through dense groves of jack oaks, with tree-tops far below him on his left hand, and the hills far above him on his right. He crawled along like some minute, wingless variety of fly.

He ate some hardtack, sauced with wild berries, when he reached the summit of the ridge, and sat there for some time, looking down into his home coulé.

Sombre, pathetic figure! His wide, round gray eyes gazing down into the beautiful valley, seeing and not seeing, the splendid cloud-shadows sweeping over the western hills and across the green and yellow wheat far below. His head drooped forward on his palm, his shoulders took on a tired stoop, his cheek-bones showed painfully. An observer might have said, "He is looking down upon his own grave."

Sunday comes in a Western wheat-harvest with such sweet and sudden relaxation to man and beast that it would be holy for that reason, if for no other, and Sundays are usually fair in harvest-time. As one goes out into the field in the hot morning sunshine, with no sound abroad save the crickets and the indescribably pleasant, silken rustling of the ripened grain, the reaper and the very sheaves in the stubble seem to be resting, dreaming.

Around the house, in the shade of the trees, the men sit, smoking, dozing, or reading the papers, while the women, never resting, move about at the housework. The men eat on Sundays about the same as on other days, and breakfast is no sooner over and out of the way than dinner begins.

But at the Smith farm there were no men dozing or reading. Mrs. Smith was alone with her three children, Mary, nine, Tommy, six, and little Ted, just past four. Her farm, rented to a neighbor, lay at the head of a coulé or narrow gulley, made at some far-off post-glacial period by the vast and angry floods of water which gullied these tremendous furrows in the level prairie—furrows so deep that undisturbed portions of the original level rose like hills on either side—rose to quite considerable mountains.

The chickens wakened her as usual that Sabbath

morning from dreams of her absent husband, from whom she had not heard for weeks. The shadows drifted over the hills, down the slopes, across the wheat, and up the opposite wall in leisurely way, as if, being Sunday, they could take it easy also. The fowls clustered about the housewife as she went out into the yard. Fuzzy little chickens swarmed out from the coops where their clucking and perpetually disgruntled mothers tramped about, petulantly thrusting their heads through the spaces between the slats.

A cow called in a deep, musical bass, and a calf answered from a little pen near by, and a pig scurried guiltily out of the cabbages. Seeing all this, seeing the pig in the cabbages, the tangle of grass in the garden, the broken fence which she had mended again and again—the little woman, hardly more than a girl, sat down and cried. The bright Sabbath morning was only a mockery without him!

A few years ago they had bought this farm, paying part, mortgaging the rest in the usual way. Edward Smith was a man of terrible energy. He worked "nights and Sundays," as the saying goes, to clear the farm of its brush and of its insatiate mortgage! In the midst of his herculean struggle came the call for volunteers, and with the grim and unselfish devotion to his country which made the Eagle Brigade able to "whip its weight in wild-cats," he threw down his scythe and grub-axe, turned his cattle loose, and became a bluecoated cog in a vast machine for killing men, and not thistles. While the millionaire sent his money to England for safekeeping, this man, with his girl-wife and

three babies, left them on a mortgaged farm, and went
away to fight for an idea. It was foolish, but it was
sublime for all that.

That was three years before, and the young wife,
sitting on the well-curb on this bright Sabbath harvest
morning, was righteously rebellious. It seemed to her
that she had borne her share of the country's sorrow.
Two brothers had been killed, the renter in whose
hands her husband had left the farm had proved a villain, one year the farm had been without crops, and
now the over-ripe grain was waiting the tardy hand of
the neighbor who had rented it, and who was cutting
his own grain first.

About six weeks before, she had received a letter
saying, "We'll be discharged in a little while." But no
other word had come from him. She had seen by the
papers that his army was being discharged, and from
day to day other soldiers slowly percolated in blue
streams back into the State and county, but still *her*
hero did not return.

Each week she had told the children that he was
coming, and she had watched the road so long that it
had become unconscious, and as she stood at the well,
or by the kitchen door, her eyes were fixed unthinkingly on the road that wound down the coulé.

Nothing wears on the human soul like waiting. If
the stranded mariner, searching the sun-bright seas,
could once give up hope of a ship, that horrible grinding on his brain would cease. It was this waiting,
hoping, on the edge of despair, that gave Emma Smith
no rest.

Neighbors said, with kind intentions, "He's sick, maybe, an' can't start north just yet. He'll come along one o' these days."

"Why don't he write?" was her question, which silenced them all. This Sunday morning it seemed to her as if she could not stand it longer. The house seemed intolerably lonely. So she dressed the little ones in their best calico dresses and home-made jackets, and closing up the house, set off down the coulé to old Mother Gray's.

"Old Widder Gray" lived at the "mouth of the coolly." She was a widow woman with a large family of stalwart boys and laughing girls. She was the visible incarnation of hospitality and optimistic poverty. With Western open-heartedness she fed every mouth that asked food of her, and worked herself to death as cheerfully as her girls danced in the neighborhood harvest dances.

She waddled down the path to meet Mrs. Smith with a broad smile on her face.

"Oh, you little dears! Come right to your granny. Gimme a kiss! Come right in, Mis' Smith. How are yeh, anyway? Nice mornin', ain't it? Come in an' set down. Everything's in a clutter, but that won't scare you any."

She led the way into the best room, a sunny, square room, carpeted with a faded and patched rag carpet, and papered with white-and-green-striped wall-paper, where a few faded effigies of dead members of the family hung in variously-sized oval walnut frames. The house resounded with singing, laughter, whistling, tramping of heavy boots, and riotous scufflings. Half-grown boys came to the door and crooked their fingers at the children, who ran out, and were soon heard in the midst of the fun.

"Don't s'pose you've heard from Ed?" Mrs. Smith shook her head. "He'll turn up some day, when you ain't lookin' for 'm." The good old soul had said that so many times that poor Mrs. Smith derived no comfort from it any longer.

"Liz heard from Al the other day. He's comin' some day this week. Anyhow, they expect him."

"Did he say anything of—"

"No, he didn't," Mrs. Gray admitted. "But then it was only a short letter, anyhow. Al ain't much for writin', anyhow.—But come out and see my new cheese. I tell yeh, I don't believe I ever had better luck in my life. If Ed should come, I want you should take him up a piece of this cheese."

It was beyond human nature to resist the influence of that noisy, hearty, loving household, and in the midst of the singing and laughing the wife forgot her anxiety, for the time at least, and laughed and sang with the rest.

About eleven o'clock a wagon-load more drove up to the door, and Billy Gray, the widow's oldest son, and his whole family, from Sand Lake Coulé, piled out amid a good-natured uproar. Everyone talked at once, except Bill, who sat in the wagon with his wrists on his knees, a straw in his mouth, and an amused twinkle in his blue eyes.

"Ain't heard nothin' o' Ed, I s'pose?" he asked in a kind of bellow. Mrs. Smith shook her head. Bill, with a delicacy very striking in such a great giant, rolled his quid in his mouth, and said:

"Didn't know but you had. I heard two or three of the Sand Lake boys are comin'. Left New Orleenes some time this week. Didn't write nothin' about Ed, but no news is good news in such cases, Mother always says."

"Well, go put out yer team," said Mrs. Gray, "an' go 'n bring me in some taters, an', Sim, you go see if you c'n find some corn. Sadie, you put on the water to bile. Come now, hustle your boots, all o' yeh. If I feed this yer crowd, we've got to have some raw materials. If y' think I'm goin' to feed yeh on pie—you're jest mightily mistaken."

The children went off into the fields, the girls put dinner on to boil, and then went to change their dresses and fix their hair. "Somebody might come," they said.

"Land sakes, I *hope* not! I don't know where in time I'd set 'em, 'less they'd eat at the second table," Mrs. Gray laughed, in pretended dismay.

The two older boys, who had served their time in the army, lay out on the grass before the house, and whittled and talked desultorily about the war and the crops, and planned buying a threshing-machine. The older girls and Mrs. Smith helped enlarge the table and put on the dishes, talking all the time in that cheery, incoherent and meaningful way a group of such women have—a conversation to be taken for its spirit rather than for its letter, though Mrs. Gray at last got the ear of them all and dissertated at length on girls.

"Girls in love ain't no use in the whole blessed

week," she said. "Sundays they're a-lookin' down the road, expectin' he'll *come*. Sunday afternoons they can't think o' nothin' else, 'cause he's *here*. Monday mornin's they're sleepy and kind o' dreamy and slimpsy, and good f'r nothin' on Tuesday and Wednesday. Thursday they git absent-minded, an' begin to look off towards Sunday agin, an' mope aroun' and let the dishwater git cold, right under their noses. Friday they break dishes, an' go off in the best room an' snivel, an' look out o' the winder. Saturdays they have queer spurts o' workin' like all p'ssessed, an' spurts o' frizzin' their hair. An' Sunday they begin it all over agin."

The girls giggled and blushed all through this tirade from their mother, their broad faces and powerful frames anything but suggestive of lackadaisical sentiment. But Mrs. Smith said:

"Now, Mrs. Gray, I hadn't ought to stay to dinner. You've got—"

"Now you set right down! If any of them girls' beaus comes, they'll have to take what's left, that's all. They ain't s'posed to have much appetite, nohow. No, you're goin' to stay if they starve, an' they ain't no danger o' that."

At one o'clock the long table was piled with boiled potatoes, cords of boiled corn on the cob, squash and pumpkin pies, hot biscuit, sweet pickles, bread and butter, and honey. Then one of the girls took down a conch-shell from a nail, and going to the door, blew a long, fine, free blast, that showed there was no weakness of lungs in her ample chest.

Then the children came out of the forest of corn,

out of the creek, out of the loft of the barn, and out of the garden.

"They come to their feed f'r all the world jest like the pigs when y' holler 'poo—ee!' See 'em scoot!" laughed Mrs. Gray, every wrinkle on her face shining with delight.

The men shut up their jack-knives, and surrounded the horse-trough to souse their faces in the cold, hard water, and in a few moments the table was filled with a merry crowd, and a row of wistful-eyed youngsters circled the kitchen wall, where they stood first on one leg and then on the other, in impatient hunger.

"Now pitch in, Mrs. Smith," said Mrs. Gray, presiding over the table. "You know these men critters. They'll eat every grain of it, if yeh give 'em a chance. I swan, they're made o' India-rubber, their stomachs is, I know it."

"Haf to eat to work," said Bill, gnawing a cob with a swift, circular motion that rivalled a corn-sheller in results.

"More like workin' to eat," put in one of the girls, with a giggle. "More eat 'n' work with you."

"*You* needn't say anything, Net. Anyone that'll eat seven ears—"

"I didn't, no such thing. You piled your cobs on my plate."

"That'll do to tell Ed Varney. It won't go down here where we know yeh."

"Good land! Eat all yeh want! They's plenty more in the fiel's, but I can't afford to give you young uns tea. The tea is for us women-folks, and 'specially f'r Mis'

Smith an' Bill's wife. We're agoin' to tell fortunes by it."

One by one the men filled up and shoved back, and one by one the children slipped into their places, and by two o'clock the women alone remained around the debris-covered table, sipping their tea and telling fortunes.

As they got well down to the grounds in the cup, they shook them with a circular motion of the hand, and then turned them bottom-side up quickly in the saucer, then twirled them three or four times one way, and three or four times the other, during a breathless pause. Then Mrs. Gray lifted the cup, and, gazing into it with profound gravity, pronounced the impending fate.

It must be admitted that, to a critical observer, she had abundant preparation for hitting close to the mark, as when she told the girls that "somebody was comin'."

"It's a man," she went on gravely. "He is cross-eyed—"

"Oh, you hush!" cried Nettie.

"He has red hair, and is death on b'iled corn and hot biscuit."

The others shrieked with delight.

"But he's goin' to get the mitten, that red-headed feller is, for I see another feller comin' up behind him."

"Oh, lemme see, lemme see!" cried Nettie.

"Keep off," said the priestess, with a lofty gesture. "His hair is black. He don't eat so much, and he works more."

The girls exploded in a shriek of laughter, and pounded their sister on the back.

At last came Mrs. Smith's turn, and she was trembling with excitement as Mrs. Gray again composed her jolly face to what she considered a proper solemnity of expression.

"Somebody is comin' to *you*," she said, after a long pause. "He's got a musket on his back. He's a soldier. He's almost here. See?"

She pointed at two little tea-stems, which really formed a faint suggestion of a man with a musket on his back. He had climbed nearly to the edge of the cup. Mrs. Smith grew pale with excitement. She trembled so she could hardly hold the cup in her hand as she gazed into it.

"It's Ed," cried the old woman. "He's on the way home. Heavens an' earth! There he is now!" She turned and waved her hand out toward the road. They rushed to the door and looked where she pointed.

A man in a blue coat, with a musket on his back, was toiling slowly up the hill on the sun-bright, dusty road, toiling slowly, with bent head half hidden by a heavy knapsack. So tired it seemed that walking was indeed a process of falling. So eager to get home he would not stop, would not look aside, but plodded on, amid the cries of the locusts, the welcome of the crickets, and the rustle of the yellow wheat. Getting back to God's country, and his wife and babies!

Laughing, crying, trying to call him and the children at the same time, the little wife, almost hysterical, snatched her hat and ran out into the yard. But the soldier had disappeared over the hill into the hollow beyond, and, by the time she had found the children, he was too far away for her voice to reach him. And, besides, she was not sure it was her husband, for he

had not turned his head at their shouts. This seemed
so strange. Why didn't he stop to rest at his old neighbor's house? Tortured by hope and doubt, she hurried
up the coulé as fast as she could push the baby wagon,
the blue-coated figure just ahead pushing steadily, silently forward up the coulé.

When the excited, panting little group came in sight
of the gate they saw the blue-coated figure standing,
leaning upon the rough rail fence, his chin on his
palms, gazing at the empty house. His knapsack, canteen, blankets, and musket lay upon the dusty grass at
his feet.

He was like a man lost in a dream. His wide, hungry
eyes devoured the scene. The rough lawn, the little un-
painted house, the field of clear yellow wheat behind
it, down across which streamed the sun, now almost
ready to touch the high hill to the west, the crickets
crying merrily, a cat on the fence near by, dreaming,
unmindful of the stranger in blue—

How peaceful it all was. O God! How far removed
from all camps, hospitals, battle lines. A little cabin
in a Wisconsin coulé, but it was majestic in its peace.
How did he ever leave it for those years of tramping,
thirsting, killing?

Trembling, weak with emotion, her eyes on the silent
figure, Mrs. Smith hurried up to the fence. Her feet
made no noise in the dust and grass, and they were
close upon him before he knew of them. The oldest boy
ran a little ahead. He will never forget that figure, that
face. It will always remain as something epic, that return of the private. He fixed his eyes on the pale face
covered with a ragged beard.

"Who *are* you, sir?" asked the wife, or, rather, started to ask, for he turned, stood a moment, and then cried:

"Emma!"

"Edward!"

The children stood in a curious row to see their mother kiss this bearded, strange man, the elder girl sobbing sympathetically with her mother. Illness had left the soldier partly deaf, and this added to the strangeness of his manner.

But the youngest child stood away, even after the girl had recognized her father and kissed him. The man turned then to the baby, and said in a curiously unpaternal tone:

"Come here, my little man; don't you know me?" But the baby backed away under the fence and stood peering at him critically.

"My little man!" What meaning in those words! This baby seemed like some other woman's child, and not the infant he had left in his wife's arms. The war had come between him and his baby—he was only a strange man to him, with big eyes; a soldier, with mother hanging to his arm, and talking in a loud voice.

"And this is Tom," the private said, drawing the oldest boy to him. "*He'll* come and see me. *He* knows his poor old pap when he comes home from the war."

The mother heard the pain and reproach in his voice and hastened to apologize.

"You've changed so, Ed. He can't know yeh. This is papa, Teddy; come and kiss him—Tom and Mary do. Come, won't you?" But Teddy still peered through the fence with solemn eyes, well out of reach. He resembled

a half-wild kitten that hesitates, studying the tones of
one's voice.

"I'll fix him," said the soldier, and sat down to undo
his knapsack, out of which he drew three enormous
and very red apples. After giving one to each of the
older children he said:

"*Now* I guess he'll come. Eh, my little man? Now
come see your pap."

Teddy crept slowly under the fence, assisted by the
over-zealous Tommy, and a moment later was kicking
and squalling in his father's arms. Then they entered
the house, into the sitting-room, poor, bare, art-forsaken
little room, too, with its rag carpet, its square clock,
and its two or three chromos and pictures from
Harper's Weekly pinned about.

"Emma, I'm all tired out," said Private Smith, as he
flung himself down on the carpet as he used to do,
while his wife brought a pillow to put under his head,
and the children stood about munching their apples.

"Tommy, you run and get me a pan of chips, and
Mary, you get the tea-kettle on, and I'll go and make
some biscuit."

And the soldier talked. Question after question he
poured forth about the crops, the cattle, the renter, the
neighbors. He slipped his heavy government brogan
shoes off his poor, tired, blistered feet, and lay out with
utter, sweet relaxation. He was a free man again, no
longer a soldier under command. At supper he
stopped once, listened and smiled. "That's old Spot.
I know her voice. I s'pose that's her calf out there in
the pen. I can't milk her to-night, though. I'm too

tired. But I tell you, I'd like a drink o' her milk. What's become of old Rove?"

"He died last winter. Poisoned, I guess." There was a moment of sadness for them all. It was some time before the husband spoke again, in a voice that trembled a little.

"Poor old feller! He'd 'a' known me a half a mile away. I expected him to come down the hill to meet me. It 'ud 'a' been more like comin' home if I could 'a' seen him comin' down the road an' waggin' his tail, an' laughin' that way he has. I tell yeh, it kind o' took hold o' me to see the blinds down an' the house shut up."

"But, yeh see, we—we expected you'd write again 'fore you started. And then we thought we'd see you if you *did* come," she hastened to explain.

"Well, I ain't worth a cent on writin'. Besides, it's just as well yeh didn't know when I was comin'. I tell you, it sounds good to hear them chickens out there, an' turkeys an' the crickets. Do you know they don't have just the same kind o' crickets down south? Who's Sam hired t' help cut yer grain?"

"The Ramsey boys."

"Looks like a good crop; but I'm afraid I won't do much gettin' it cut. This cussed fever an' ague has got me down pretty low. I don't know when I'll get rid of it. I'll bet I've took twenty-five pounds of quinine if I've taken a bit. Gimme another biscuit. I tell yeh, they taste good, Emma. I ain't had anything like it— Say, if you'd 'a' hear'd me braggin' to th' boys about your butter 'n' biscuits I'll bet your ears 'ud 'a' burnt."

The private's wife colored with pleasure. "Oh, you're always a-braggin' about your things. Everybody makes good butter."

"Yes; old lady Snyder, for instance."

"Oh, well, she ain't to be mentioned. She's Dutch."

"Or old Mis' Snively. One more cup o' tea, Mary. That's my girl! I'm feeling better already. I just b'lieve the matter with me is, I'm *starved*."

This was a delicious hour, one long to be remembered. They were like lovers again. But their tenderness, like that of a typical American family, found utterance in tones, rather than in words. He was praising her when praising her biscuit, and she knew it. They grew soberer when he showed where he had been struck, one ball burning the back of his hand, one cutting away a lock of hair from his temple, and one passing through the calf of his leg. The wife shuddered to think how near she had come to being a soldier's widow. Her waiting no longer seemed hard. This sweet, glorious hour effaced it all.

Then they rose, and all went out into the garden and down to the barn. He stood beside her while she milked old Spot. They began to plan fields and crops for the next year.

His farm was weedy and encumbered, a rascally renter had run away with his machinery (departing between two days), his children needed clothing, the years were coming upon him, he was sick and emaciated, but his heroic soul did not quail. With the same courage with which he had faced his Southern march he entered upon a still more hazardous future.

Oh, that mystic hour! The pale man with big eyes

standing there by the well, with his young wife by his side. The vast moon swinging above the eastern peaks, the cattle winding down the pasture slopes with jangling bells, the crickets singing, the stars blooming out sweet and far and serene; the katydids rhythmetically calling, the little turkeys crying querulously, as they settled to roost in the poplar tree near the open gate. The voices at the well drop lower, the little ones nestle in their father's arms at last, and Teddy falls asleep there.

The common soldier of the American volunteer army had returned. His war with the South was over, and his fight, his daily running fight with nature and against the injustice of his fellowmen, was begun again.

1890

IN FLANDERS FIELDS

JOHN MCCRAE

In Flanders fields the poppies blow
Between the crosses, row on row,
That mark our place; and in the sky
The larks, still bravely singing, fly
Scarce heard amid the guns below.

We are the Dead. Short days ago
We lived, felt dawn, saw sunset glow,
Loved, and were loved, and now we lie
In Flanders fields.

Take up our quarrel with the foe:
To you from failing hands we throw
The torch; be yours to hold it high.
If ye break faith with us who die
We shall not sleep, though poppies grow
In Flanders fields.

1919

From ON A NOTE OF TRIUMPH: VE-DAY, 1945

NORMAN CORWIN

But what do we know now that we didn't know before?
What have we LEARNED out of this war?

For one thing, Evil is not always as insidious as advertised
But will, upon occasion, give fair warning, just as
smoke announces the intention of flame to follow.
This is one due you must give the devil.
Satan, whose fine Italian hand is in the writing of
Mein Kampf, was, together with the paper-hanger,
perfectly candid about the blueprints.
Between them they announced they were going to lie
and plunder, and they kept their word.

Never has disaster had so many heralds as this war:
Cassandra spoke from every lecture platform, and the
notices were posted high and low:
A cabinet minister resigned at Downing Street, protesting;
A President cried, "Quarantine!"
Moscow sent food and guns to Barcelona;
A housewife of Duluth boycotted German goods;

An emperor of Ethiopia said in good French before the
     statesmen of Geneva:
*Je suis venu pour avertir l'Europe de la catastrophe
     qui lui attend.*
     I came to give Europe warning of the doom that
     awaits it.
*Je suis venue pour defendre la cause de tous les petites
     nations menacées d'aggression.*
     I came defending the cause of all small people
     who are threatened with aggression.
*Aujourd'hui le problème a une porte beaucoup plus
     etendus que l'aggression italienne en elle même.*
     The problem today is much wider than merely a
     question of Italian aggression; it is collective se-
     curity.
La moralité internationale est en jue.
     It is international morality which is at stake.
Dieu et l'histoire se rappelleront de votre jugement.
     God and history will remember your judgment.

Signs and portents?
It was no furtive tapping on the window sill at night,
But clamorous pounding in the public square,
Blow after blow, like a monstrous dropforge,
Beating into shape the time to come.

And the time came, and the prophecies matured:
The storm arrived, and was no surprise to the barome-
     ter:
The Jew who had cautioned...
The Nazis are not against the Jews alone—that's just

> *a sham. If you let them carry on this way, they'll*
> *be the death of Christians, too.*

... he saw gentiles die as well, and sighed,
And foraged for bullets in the cellars of the Warsaw
    ghetto.
Yea, and the time came, and it developed that Cas-
    sandra and the Jew were right and that the Clive-
    den set was wrong:
Fire and brimstone, dropping from the sky, were edu-
    cational:
There were tongues in torpedoes; sermons in bombs;
    books in the running battles.
Whatever was learned, was learned the hard way,
Between blood transfusions and last rites.

Each lesson fell trip-hammer hard, with a bang that
    killed a citizen or two somewhere:

WE'VE LEARNED OUT OF WORLD
WAR II THAT WE'D LEARNED NOTH-
ING OUT OF WORLD WAR I.

WE'VE LEARNED THAT NATIONS
WHICH DON'T KNOW WHAT THEY
WANT WILL GET WHAT THEY DON'T
WANT.

WE'VE LEARNED THAT OUR EAST
COAST IS THE WEST BANK OF THE

RHINE, AND THAT THE DEFENSES OF
SEATTLE BEGIN IN SHANGHAI.

WE LEARNED AT MUNICH THAT A
SOFT ANSWER DOESN'T TURN AWAY
WRATH; THAT IF YOU OFFER YOUR
OTHER CHEEK TO A NAZI, YOU'LL
GET YOUR HEAD BLOWN OFF.

WE'VE LEARNED THAT A NEWSPAPER
RIGHT AT HOME CAN LIE WITH A
STRAIGHT FACE SEVEN DAYS A WEEK,
AND BE AS FILTHY AND FASCIST AS A
HANDOUT IN BERLIN.

WE'VE LEARNED THAT THOSE MOST
CONCERNED WITH SAVING THE
WORLD FROM COMMUNISM USUALLY
TURN UP MAKING IT SAFE FOR FAS-
CISM.

WE'VE LEARNED THAT WOMEN CAN
WORK AND FIGHT, AS WELL AS LOOK
PRETTY AND COOK.

WE'VE LEARNED THAT THE GER-
MANS CAME CLOSE TO WINNING THE
FIRST TIME, EVEN CLOSER THE SEC-
OND TIME, AND MIGHT DAMN WELL
WIN IF WE GIVE THEM A THIRD TIME.

WE'VE LEARNED THE VALUE OF AL-

LIES IN A WORLD WHERE ANY WAR
IS SOONER OR LATER A WORLD WAR.

WE'VE LEARNED THAT SOME MEN
WILL FIGHT FOR POWER, BUT THAT
MOST MEN WILL FIGHT TO BE FREE.

WE'VE LEARNED THAT FREEDOM
ISN'T SOMETHING TO BE WON AND
THEN FORGOTTEN. IT MUST BE RE-
NEWED, LIKE SOIL AFTER YIELDING
GOOD CROPS; MUST BE REWOUND,
LIKE A FAITHFUL CLOCK; EXERCISED,
LIKE A HEALTHY MUSCLE.

These and many more—
These are the lessons our sons and brothers have
     turned to dust to teach us:
And whether Victory will stick, and the dead be not
     made fools of,
Depends on whether what we learn is held close and
     constant as a catechism,
Come summer and prosperity, come winter and the
     wolf, come ebb tide and come flood.

THE BEGINNING OF HOME

JOHN DOS PASSOS

Terry Bryant is the first man off the transport.

As he jumps out he has a whirling glimpse of ranked planes and hangars and tugs and carferries on the bay and the piled up buildings of San Francisco dim-shining through the mist. Overhead through bright tatters of mist the sky shines blue blue blue.

Not home but the beginning of home.

For a moment Terry thinks of throwing himself flat on his face and kissing the concrete runway.

What he does is to squat on his heels and give the concrete three quick pats. Getting to his feet with a queasy grin on his face he notices that the man behind him has the same idea. This is a stocky serious dark fellow who makes the gesture slowly and deliberately. He kisses the palm of his hand and presses it lovingly on the ground.

Terry catches his eye and they laugh and nod in each other's faces like a couple of jackasses.

The rest of the men come crowding behind them in mussed and varied battle dress: leather jackets with Chinese and American flags on the back, sheepskins, mottled brown and green ponchos. Nobody says anything. They look about them with big shining eyes,

like children's eyes Christmas morning, eyes big enough
to take in all America. After the warmth of Pearl the
chilly misty morning makes them shiver. With quaking
fingers they start to light cigarettes.

"No smoking, boys," intones the airport officer in
a weary voice. They stamp out their cigarettes with
eager obedience and crowd after him as he leads the
way with the papers fluttering in the breeze off the
board in his hand.

Inside the reception center it was all desks and coun-
ters round the walls, and long lines of men waiting under numbers and lettering, dragging barracksbags and
duffle as they moved.

The biggest crowd was round a milk bar attended by
two cute girls in some sort of USO uniform. Terry
couldn't keep his eyes off them as he waited his turn.
One was blond. The dark one had eyes as blue as the
sky over San Francisco. Both girls had a clean laun-
dered look. Their slender pink fingers moved deftly
among the glasses, never spilled a drop of the yellow
milk.

Prettiest sight he'd seen in four years, Terry was
telling himself as he waited his turn. He couldn't
find a word to say. All he could do was give them the
Asiatic stare. "By God," the man next to him muttered
as they were pushed away from the stand by guys edg-
ing in behind them, "they talk English."

Terry had to waste those first delicious stateside
hours standing in line and checking in, standing in
line and checking in. It took forever. Still he had a
lucky break. His service ribbons and the fact that they

were short of sergeants that day earned him a detail to
ride herd on a bunch of men scheduled to depart at
13:45. "Direct flight to Noo York," whispered the wise-
guy who stamped his orders.

It wasn't so direct as all that. The takeoff was two
hours late. There were long waits in Salt Lake City
and Omaha and at some weathered-in airfield out in
the boondocks in the Middle West. Too much coffee,
too many cigarettes. Bumpy as hell over the Alle-
ghanies. Holloweyed and desperate they ended up the
second evening in a wet snowstorm on an empty airstrip near Allentown, Pennsylvania. Flight terminated.

"What do we do now?" the guys asked each other.
The sleepy lieutenant in the transportation hut didn't
have an idea in the world. After a lot of trudging about
in the wet driving snow—and this was only October,
the guys told each other, supposed to be Indian summer in this man's country—a bunch of them chipped in
on a taxi into Philadelphia. Haggard and jangled
after all those hours in the air and the waiting and the
uncertainty, what they needed was a drink.

Just no place a man could get a drink in Pennsylvania not on a Sunday night, said the driver.

It wasn't the homecoming any of them had planned.

Ridgefield looks about the same. The house hasn't
changed, except that it needs painting. There's the
privet hedge Pop used to try to get the boys to help him
clip and the bay window and the brick steps they built
themselves up to the narrow porch that faces the street,
and the colored glass on either side of the front door.

Old torn sheets of newspaper and rags and dirt have piled up behind the hedge. The little strip of grass has a straggly look it never would have had if Pop had lived.

The front door is locked. Leaving his duffle piled on the porch Terry tiptoes around to the back. The boards of the kitchen stoop creak and give. As soon as he has his hand on the knob he smells the warm vinegar. So long as he can remember the house has smelt of pickles in the fall. His mother's square shoulders and the starched bow she's tied in her apronstrings are just as he remembered them. When she turns from the crock she's fussing over her eyes look as blue to him as that girl's eyes at the milkstand in Oakland.

Mom hasn't changed any more than her house, except that her hair is all white. In the old days before Pearl Harbor Terry used to worry about how gray it was getting.

"Terence," she says, in that unexcited way she has, as if she had seen him the night before and he hadn't been away at all. She takes hold of his elbows and looks him critically up and down. "Terence, you're two jumps ahead of a fit. . . . I got to feed you up. . . . Feeding up my boys is about the only pleasure left to an old woman like me."

She lets out one of her little gruff sudden laughs.

He hears himself explaining haltingly that Okinawa left them all jumpy.

"But that was months and months ago."

She changes the subject abruptly.

"Buddy's home on leave. Of course I never see him

except when he's asleep." She's trying to hammer some
sense of responsibility into his head, especially now
that he's an uncle.

"You're an uncle too, Terence." Mom gives him one
of her sharp straight looks. "Your sister made me a
grandmother in the shape of a bouncing boy about
six weeks ago," Mom rattles on cheerfully. "I guess you
never got our letters. . . . Buddy's asleep in there."

She opens the door of the downstairs bedroom a
crack and makes Terry look in. All he can see is a
body muffled up under the bedclothes about four times
as large as the fifteen-year-old Buddy last seen four
years ago. A gob's uniform is neatly hung over the
chair. Mom closes the door softly and they tiptoe back
to the kitchen.

"If your poor father had only lived to see this day,"
she starts to say, but her voice dries up. She starts
making a great clatter with the breakfast things over
the electric stove.

Terry finds himself following her around the kitchen
getting in her way like he used to when he was a young
fellow. He doesn't want to look so glum. He has to
think of something to make her laugh. "What do you
suppose they called me, Mom? Joisey . . . I can't imagine why that was."

Mom starts in on the neighbors. They fall to laughing easily together over funny things that happened
like they used to. It's only when Terry finds he can't
eat the fine breakfast she's cooked for him that Mom
begins to look worried again. Muttering that what the
boy needs is a good rest she helps him get his things upstairs to the room under the eaves with the twin beds

that used to be his and Buddy's in the old days. He
stretches himself out without even taking off his shoes
and falls into a dead sleep.

When they woke him to come down to dinner the
whole family was assembled. Terry didn't know which
of the women to kiss first. There was Francine and her
husband, heavylipped Fred Dirks, and the baby looking up out of a bassinet with his tiny pink face just
like his father's. There was Mom's sister Aunt Lillian,
and her husband and their daughter Jane, eighteen
already and a goodlooker and there was Buddy with
that long smooth brown face of his and the slit eyes
and a smirk on his mouth.

Mom made Terry sit at the head of the table in the
chair with arms where he remembered Pop sitting
with his glasses pushed up on his forehead to read the
evening paper. Her eyes were shining when she came
out of the kitchen with a steak for her returned service-
men. Mr. Snider the butcher had been saving it for
when Terence came home. She'd been saving up cou-
pons for three months. The rest of them would have to
eat hamburger, she said.

The steak must have been three inches thick, done
to a turn just the way he liked it. They all watched the
juice run out when he cut into it. Their eyes were all
on his face. He put a piece of steak in his mouth and
chewed and chewed but he couldn't taste a thing. His
stomach felt like a rock. He managed to swallow that
piece, but he knew that if he took another he'd throw
up. He was in a cold sweat.

"Think nothing of it, Mom," he said. "I'll make

Buddy my deputy. All those K rations shrink a guy's stomach."

"Tell me the Air Force had the best chow in the service," Buddy said as he reached over with his fork and speared the steak off Terry's plate. "I need the strength," he added with that smirk on his mouth. "I've lost ten pounds since I been home, just havin' a time."

An indulgent titter went round the table. Aunt Lillian's husband let out a guffaw.

Mom hadn't touched the food on her plate. She sat looking into Terry's face. All the blue sparkle had gone out of her eyes. The skin round them looked old and crinkled. "But it was months ago," she said again.

"Why bring that up?"

Terry felt the nasty snarl in his voice. It wasn't his fault. To hell with it.

When the women went into the kitchen to help Mom with the dishes Terry found himself out in the front hall with Buddy. Fred Dirks and Aunt Lillian's husband were smoking cigars in the living-room and arguing about what kind of a President Jimmy Byrnes would have made if he'd been Vice-President instead of Truman. Buddy came up to Terry and pulled at the lapel of his tunic. He still had that smirk on his face that rubbed Terry the wrong way while they ate.

"How about comin' out on a double date, Terry," Buddy whispered as he pushed a cigarette at him out of his pack. "I know some pretty hot numbers." He gave Terry a wink. "It's a sailor's privilege."

Terry pushed away the cigarette. He felt the frown

THE BEGINNING OF HOME

wrinkling his forehead. He wanted to wipe that damn
smirk off the kid's face.

"You need what you ain't been gettin' in the worst
way, Terry."

"None of your goddam business what I need." Terry
didn't want his voice to sound so nasty, but he couldn't
help it. "You young punks think you're the only man
ever slept with a woman."

Buddy gave his shoulders an exaggerated shrug.

Terry's fists were clenched so tight his nails cut into
his hands. He was breathing hard.

"Well I guess I'll scram," said Buddy.

"No you don't. Not till you've put on the gloves with
me." Terry's voice sounded nasty to his own ears.
"Remember how Pop used to make us put on the gloves
if we had a fallin' out?"

Buddy shook his closecropped narrow head. "No,
Terry, no." Terry plunged down the basement stairs.
Buddy followed him pleading into his ear. "Easy does
it, Terry. Easy does it."

The gloves were hanging from their old place on a
nail across from the furnace.

The sight of them brought back Pop's red round face
smiling under his mustache and the way he would
snap his suspenders while he told the boys tales of
Kelly's gymnasium and the bareknuckled brawlers
before Fitzsimmons. Pop used to make them settle it
like gentlemen if they had a falling out. "Never go to
bed in anger against your fellow man," Pop used to
say. The warm memory of good old Pop was like a
picture suddenly glanced at on the wall. It had nothing
to do with the way Terry felt now.

Buddy stood between Terry and the gloves still arguing. "Look at the dust on 'em. I'm all cleaned up to go out." There was a childish whine in his voice. "Terry, let's take it easy tonight. Mom wants us to be with her. Easy does it." He didn't want to stand up that date. "Never disappoint a woman." That smirk was back on his mouth.

"You put on those gloves before I slam you one with my bare fist."

Buddy pulled off his navy blouse and hung it carefully on a clotheshorse. The boy sure had developed a pair of shoulders. Terry caught himself feeling a sudden gush of pride in his kid brother, but it was lost in the nastiness seething up inside him.

He started sparring before Buddy had time to tie his gloves. Buddy was light on his feet. He kept his gloves up and parried and ducked. Terry could see he was pulling his punches. That made him all the madder.

He swung at Buddy and Buddy came back with a tap on his jaw. There was the black taste of blood in his mouth. He dove at Buddy with both fists. Buddy came back a little harder.

Terry couldn't stop that left. He had a cut on his lip. He wanted to kill him. He started swinging.

Mom's voice brought him up sharp. "Terence." Buddy had backed off and lifted his gloves above his head. "Have a heart, Terry . . . I'm not fightin' you."

Their mother was standing on the stairs behind them. Terry could see the whites all around her eyes. Her mouth made an "O." "Terence," she cried again in a voice like breaking glass.

He shook his hands free of the gloves. "Someday

I'll kill the little smart alec," he hissed out of the corner of his mouth as he brushed past her. He stamped up the two flights to his room and slammed the door behind him and locked it on the inside like he used to when he had a tantrum as a little kid. Then he let himself drop down on the bed.

He couldn't sleep. He couldn't even stay on the bed. He spent the night pacing up and down the room.

Next morning before anybody was up he got a few things together in an overnight bag.

He wrote a note to leave on the kitchen table:

> Mom tell Buddy I'm sorry. It's what they call battle fatigue. I've seen the symptoms often enough to know what they are. I figured I'd better get fixed up before I got separated from the service. I'll write and call up. Don't worry.

1961

From HIROSHIMA DIARY

MICHIHIKO HACHIYA, M.D.

6 August 1945

The hour was early; the morning still, warm, and beautiful. Shimmering leaves, reflecting sunlight from a cloudless sky, made a pleasant contrast with shadows in my garden as I gazed absently through wide-flung doors opening to the south.

Clad in drawers and undershirt, I was sprawled on the living room floor exhausted because I had just spent a sleepless night on duty as an air warden in my hospital.

Suddenly, a strong flash of light startled me—and then another. So well does one recall little things that I remember vividly how a stone lantern in the garden became brilliantly lit and I debated whether this light was caused by a magnesium flare or sparks from a passing trolley.

Garden shadows disappeared. The view where a moment before all had been so bright and sunny was now dark and hazy. Through swirling dust I could barely discern a wooden column that had supported one corner of my house. It was leaning crazily and the roof sagged dangerously.

Moving instinctively, I tried to escape, but rubble and fallen timbers barred the way. By picking my way cautiously I managed to reach the *rōka* and stepped down into my garden. A profound weakness overcame me, so I stopped to regain my strength. To my surprise I discovered that I was completely naked. How odd! Where were my drawers and undershirt?

What had happened?

All over the right side of my body I was cut and bleeding. A large splinter was protruding from a mangled wound in my thigh, and something warm trickled into my mouth. My cheek was torn, I discovered as I felt it gingerly, with the lower lip laid wide open. Embedded in my neck was a sizable fragment of glass which I matter-of-factly dislodged, and with the detachment of one stunned and shocked I studied it and my blood-stained hand.

Where was my wife?

Suddenly thoroughly alarmed, I began to yell for her: "Yaeko-san! Yaeko-san! Where are you?"

Blood began to spurt. Had my carotid artery been cut? Would I bleed to death? Frightened and irrational, I called out again: "It's a five-hundred-ton bomb! Yaeko-san, where are you? A five-hundred-ton bomb has fallen!"

Yaeko-san, pale and frightened, her clothes torn and blood-stained, emerged from the ruins of our house holding her elbow. Seeing her, I was reassured. My own panic assuaged, I tried to reassure her.

"We'll be all right," I explained. "Only let's get out of here as fast as we can."

She nodded, and I motioned for her to follow me.

The shortest path to the street lay through the house next door so through the house we went—running, stumbling, falling, and then running again until in headlong flight we tripped over something and fell sprawling into the street. Getting to my feet, I discovered that I had tripped over a man's head.

"Excuse me! Excuse me, please!" I cried hysterically.

There was no answer. The man was dead. The head had belonged to a young officer whose body was crushed beneath a massive gate.

We stood in the street, uncertain and afraid, until a house across from us began to sway and then with a rending motion fell almost at our feet. Our own house began to sway, and in a minute it, too, collapsed in a cloud of dust. Other buildings caved in or toppled. Fires sprang up and whipped by a vicious wind began to spread.

It finally dawned on us that we could not stay there in the street, so we turned our steps towards the hospital. Our home was gone; we were wounded and needed treatment; and after all, it was my duty to be with my staff. This latter was an irrational thought—what good could I be to anyone, hurt as I was.

We started out, but after twenty or thirty steps I had to stop. My breath became short, my heart pounded, and my legs gave way under me. An overpowering thirst seized me and I begged Yaeko-san to find me some water. But there was no water to be found. After a little my strength somewhat returned and we were able to go on.

I was still naked, and although I did not feel the

least bit of shame, I was disturbed to realize that modesty had deserted me. On rounding a corner we came upon a soldier standing idly in the street. He had a towel draped across his shoulder, and I asked if he would give it to me to cover my nakedness. The soldier surrendered the towel quite willingly but said not a word. A little later I lost the towel, and Yaeko-san took off her apron and tied it around my loins.

Our progress towards the hospital was interminably slow, until finally, my legs, stiff from drying blood, refused to carry me farther. The strength, even the will, to go on deserted me, so I told my wife, who was almost as badly hurt as I, to go on alone. This she objected to, but there was no choice. She had to go ahead and try to find someone to come back for me.

Yaeko-san looked into my face for a moment, and then, without saying a word, turned away and began running towards the hospital. Once, she looked back and waved and in a moment she was swallowed up in the gloom. It was quite dark now, and with my wife gone, a feeling of dreadful loneliness overcame me.

I must have gone out of my head lying there in the road because the next thing I recall was discovering that the clot on my thigh had been dislodged and blood was again spurting from the wound. I pressed my hand to the bleeding area and after a while the bleeding stopped and I felt better.

Could I go on?

I tried. It was all a nightmare—my wounds, the darkness, the road ahead. My movements were ever so slow; only my mind was running at top speed.

In time I came to an open space where the houses had been removed to make a fire lane. Through the dim light I could make out ahead of me the hazy outlines of the Communications Bureau's big concrete building, and beyond it the hospital. My spirits rose because I knew that now someone would find me; and if I should die, at least my body would be found.

I paused to rest. Gradually things around me came into focus. There were the shadowy forms of people, some of whom looked like walking ghosts. Others moved as though in pain, like scarecrows, their arms held out from their bodies with forearms and hands dangling. These people puzzled me until I suddenly realized that they had been burned and were holding their arms out to prevent the painful friction of raw surfaces rubbing together. A naked woman carrying a naked baby came into view. I averted my gaze. Perhaps they had been in the bath. But then I saw a naked man, and it occurred to me that, like myself, some strange thing had deprived them of their clothes. An old woman lay near me with an expression of suffering on her face; but she made no sound. Indeed, one thing was common to everyone I saw—complete silence.

All who could were moving in the direction of the hospital. I joined in the dismal parade when my strength was somewhat recovered, and at last reached the gates of the Communications Bureau.

Familiar surroundings, familiar faces. There was Mr. Iguchi and Mr. Yoshihiro and my old friend, Mr. Sera, the head of the business office. They hastened to give me a hand, their expressions of pleasure changing to alarm when they saw that I was hurt. I was too happy to see them to share their concern.

No time was lost over greetings. They eased me onto a stretcher and carried me into the Communications Building, ignoring my protests that I could walk. Later, I learned that the hospital was so overrun that the Communications Bureau had to be used as an emergency hospital. The rooms and corridors were crowded with people, many of whom I recognized as neighbors. To me it seemed that the whole community was there.

My friends passed me through an open window into a janitor's room recently converted to an emergency first-aid station. The room was a shambles; fallen plaster, broken furniture, and debris littered the floor; the walls were cracked; and a heavy steel window casement was twisted and almost wrenched from its seating. What a place to dress the wounds of the injured.

To my great surprise who should appear but my private nurse, Miss Kado, and Mr. Mizoguchi, and old Mrs. Saeki. Miss Kado set about examining my wounds without speaking a word. No one spoke. I asked for a shirt and pajamas. They got them for me, but still no one spoke. Why was everyone so quiet?

Miss Kado finished the examination, and in a moment it felt as if my chest was on fire. She had begun to paint my wounds with iodine and no amount of entreaty would make her stop. With no alternative but to endure the iodine, I tried to divert myself by looking out the window.

The hospital lay directly opposite with part of the roof and the third floor sunroom in plain view, and as I looked up, I witnessed a sight which made me forget my smarting wounds. Smoke was pouring out of the sunroom windows. The hospital was afire!

"Fire!" I shouted. "Fire! Fire! The hospital is on fire!"

My friends looked up. It was true. The hospital *was* on fire.

The alarm was given and from all sides people took up the cry. The high-pitched voice of Mr. Sera, the business officer, rose above the others, and it seemed as if his was the first voice I had heard that day. The uncanny stillness was broken. Our little world was now in pandemonium.

I remember that Dr. Sasada, chief of the Pediatric Service, came in and tried to reassure me, but I could scarcely hear him above the din. I heard Dr. Hinoi's voice and then Dr. Koyama's. Both were shouting orders to evacuate the hospital and with such vigor that it sounded as though the sheer strength of their voices could hasten those who were slow to obey.

The sky became bright as flames from the hospital mounted. Soon the Bureau was threatened and Mr. Sera gave the order to evacuate. My stretcher was moved into a rear garden and placed beneath an old cherry tree. Other patients limped into the garden or were carried until soon the entire area became so crowded that only the very ill had room to lie down. No one talked, and the ominous silence was relieved only by a subdued rustle among so many people, restless, in pain, anxious, and afraid, waiting for something else to happen.

The sky filled with black smoke and glowing sparks. Flames rose and the heat set currents of air in motion. Updrafts became so violent that sheets of zinc roofing were hurled aloft and released, humming and twirling, in erratic flight. Pieces of flaming wood soared and fell like fiery swallows. While I was trying to beat out the flames, a hot ember seared my ankle. It was all I could do to keep from being burned alive.

The Bureau started to burn, and window after window became a square of flame until the whole structure was converted into a crackling, hissing inferno.

Scorching winds howled around us, whipping dust and ashes into our eyes and up our noses. Our mouths became dry, our throats raw and sore from the biting smoke pulled into our lungs. Coughing was uncontrollable. We would have moved back, but a group of wooden barracks behind us caught fire and began to burn like tinder.

The heat finally became too intense to endure, and we were left no choice but to abandon the garden. Those who could fled; those who could not perished. Had it not been for my devoted friends, I would have died, but again, they came to the rescue and carried my stretcher to the main gate on the other side of the Bureau.

Here, a small group of people were already clustered, and here I found my wife. Dr. Sasada and Miss Kado joined us.

Fires sprang up on every side as violent winds

fanned flames from one building to another. Soon, we were surrounded. The ground we held in front of the Communications Bureau became an oasis in a desert of fire. As the flames came closer the heat became more intense, and if someone in our group had not had the presence of mind to drench us with water from a fire hose, I doubt if anyone could have survived.

Hot as it was, I began to shiver. The drenching was too much. My heart pounded; things began to whirl until all before me blurred.

"*Kurushii*," I murmured weakly. "I am done."

The sound of voices reached my ears as though from a great distance and finally became louder as if close at hand. I opened my eyes; Dr. Sasada was feeling my pulse. What had happened? Miss Kado gave me an injection. My strength gradually returned. I must have fainted.

Huge raindrops began to fall. Some thought a thunderstorm was beginning and would extinguish the fires. But these drops were capricious. A few fell and then a few more and that was all the rain we saw.

The first floor of the Bureau was now ablaze and flames were spreading rapidly towards our little oasis by the gate. Right then, I could hardly understand the situation, much less do anything about it.

An iron window frame, loosened by fire, crashed to the ground behind us. A ball of fire whizzed by me, setting my clothes ablaze. They drenched me with water again. From then on I am confused as to what happened.

I do remember Dr. Hinoi because of the pain, the

pain I felt when he jerked me to my feet. I remember
being moved or rather dragged, and my whole spirit
rebelling against the torment I was made to endure.

My next memory is of an open area. The fires must
have receded. I was alive. My friends had somehow
managed to rescue me again.

A head popped out of an air-raid dugout, and I
heard the unmistakable voice of old Mrs. Saeki: "Cheer
up, Doctor! Everything will be all right. The north
side is burnt out. We have nothing further to fear
from the fire."

I might have been her son, the way the old lady
calmed and reassured me. And indeed, she was right.
The entire northern side of the city was completely
burned. The sky was still dark, but whether it was
evening or midday I could not tell. It might even have
been the next day. Time had no meaning. What I had
experienced might have been crowded into a moment
or been endured through the monotony of eternity.

Smoke was still rising from the second floor of the
hospital, but the fire had stopped. There was nothing
left to burn, I thought; but later I learned that the first
floor of the hospital had escaped destruction largely
through the courageous efforts of Dr. Koyama and Dr.
Hinoi.

The streets were deserted except for the dead. Some
looked as if they had been frozen by death while in
the full action of flight; others lay sprawled as though
some giant had flung them to their death from a great
height.

Hiroshima was no longer a city, but a burnt-over

prairie. To the east and to the west everything was
flattened. The distant mountains seemed nearer than
I could ever remember. The hills of Ushita and the
woods of Nigitsu loomed out of the haze and smoke
like the nose and eyes on a face. How small Hiroshima
was with its houses gone.

The wind changed and the sky again darkened with
smoke.

Suddenly, I heard someone shout: "Planes! Enemy
planes!"

Could that be possible after what had already happened? What was there left to bomb? My thoughts
were interrupted by the sound of a familiar name.

A nurse calling Dr. Katsube.

"It is Dr. Katsube! It's him!" shouted old Mrs. Saeki,
a happy ring to her voice. "Dr. Katsube has come!"

It was Dr. Katsube, our head surgeon, but he seemed
completely unaware of us as he hurried past, making a
straight line for the hospital. Enemy planes were forgotten, so great was our happiness that Dr. Katsube had
been spared to return to us.

Before I could protest, my friends were carrying me
into the hospital. The distance was only a hundred
meters, but it was enough to cause my heart to pound
and make me sick and faint.

I recall the hard table and the pain when my face
and lip were sutured, but I have no recollection of the
forty or more other wounds Dr. Katsube closed before
night.

They removed me to an adjoining room, and I remember feeling relaxed and sleepy. The sun had gone

down, leaving a dark red sky. The red flames of the burning city had scorched the heavens. I gazed at the sky until sleep overtook me.

7 August 1945

I must have slept soundly because when I opened my eyes a piercing hot sun was shining in on me. There were no shutters or curtains to lessen the glare— and for that matter no windows. The groans of patients assaulted my ears. Everything was in a turmoil.

Instruments, window frames, and debris littered the floor. The walls and ceilings were scarred and picked as though someone had sprinkled sesame seeds over their surfaces. Most of the marks had been made by slivers of flying glass but the larger scars had been caused by hurtling instruments and pieces of window casements.

Near a window an instrument cabinet was overturned. The head piece had been knocked off the ear, nose, and throat examining chair, and a broken sunlamp was overturned across the seat. I saw nothing that was not broken or in disorder.

Dr. Sasada, who had looked after me yesterday, lay on my left. I had thought he escaped injury, but now I could see that he was badly burned. His arms and hands were bandaged and his childish face so obscured by swelling that I would not have recognized him had it not been for his voice.

My wife lay to my right. Her face was covered with

a white ointment, giving her a ghostly appearance. Her right arm was in a sling.

Miss Kado, only slightly wounded, was between me and my wife. She had nursed all of us throughout the night.

My wife, seeing that I was awake, turned and said: "Last night, you seemed to be suffering."

"Yes," said Miss Kado, chiming in. "I don't know how many times I examined your breathing."

I recognized Dr. Fujii's wife sitting motionless on a bench near the wall. Her face bore an expression of anguish and despair. Turning to Miss Kado, I asked what the matter was, and she replied: "Mrs. Fujii was not hurt very much, but her baby was. It died during the night."

"Where is Dr. Fujii?" I inquired.

"Their older daughter is lost," she answered. "He's been out all night looking for her and hasn't returned."

Dr. Koyama came in to inquire how we were. The sight of him, with his head bandaged and an arm in a sling, brought tears to my eyes. He had worked all night and was even now thinking of others before himself.

Dr. Katsube, our surgeon, and Miss Takao, a surgical nurse, were with Dr. Koyama, who was now deputy director. They all looked tired and haggard, and their white clothes were dirty and blood-stained. I learned that Mr. Iguchi, our driver, had contrived to rig up an emergency operating light from a car battery and headlight with which they had managed to operate until the light went out just before day.

Dr. Koyama, observing my concern, remarked: "Doctor, everything is all right."

Dr. Katsube looked me over and after feeling my pulse, said: "You received many wounds, but they all missed vital spots."

He then described them and told me how they had been treated. I was surprised to learn that my shoulder had been severely cut but relieved at his optimism for my recovery.

"How many patients are in the hospital?" I asked Dr. Koyama.

"About a hundred and fifty," he replied. "Quite a few have died, but there are still so many that there is no place to put one's foot down. They are packed in everywhere, even the toilets."

Nodding, Dr. Katsube added: "There are about a half dozen beneath the stairway, and about fifty in the front garden of the hospital."

They discussed methods for restoring order, at least to the extent of making the corridors passable.

In the space of one night patients had become packed, like the rice in *sushi,* into every nook and cranny of the hospital. The majority were badly burned, a few severely injured. All were critically ill. Many had been near the heart of the city and in their efforts to flee managed to get only as far as the Communications Hospital before their strength failed. Others, from nearer by, came deliberately to seek treatment or because this building, standing alone where all else was destroyed, represented shelter and a place of refuge. They came as an avalanche and overran the hospital.

There was no friend or relative to minister to their needs, no one to prepare their food. Everything was in disorder. And to make matters worse was the vomiting and diarrhea. Patients who could not walk urinated and defecated where they lay. Those who could walk would feel their way to the exits and relieve themselves there. Persons entering or leaving the hospital could not avoid stepping in the filth, so closely was it spread. The front entrance became covered with feces overnight, and nothing could be done for there were no bed pans and, even if there had been, no one to carry them to the patients.

Disposing of the dead was a minor problem, but to clean the rooms and corridors of urine, feces, and vomitus was impossible.

The people who were burned suffered most because as their skin peeled away, glistening raw wounds were exposed to the heat and filth. This was the environment patients had to live in. It made one's hair stand on end, but there was no way to help the situation.

This was the pattern conversation took as I lay there and listened. It was inconceivable.

"When can I get up?" I asked Dr. Katsube. "Perhaps I can do something to help."

"Not until your sutures are out," he answered. "And that won't be for at least a week."

With that to think about they left me.

I was not left long with my thoughts. One after another the staff came in to express their concern over my injuries and to wish me a speedy recovery. Some of my visitors embarrassed me, for they appeared to be as badly injured as myself. Had it been possible, I would have concealed my whereabouts.

Dr. Nishimura, President of the Okayama Medical Association, came all the way from my native city, ninety miles away, to see me. He had been crew captain of the boat team when we were classmates in Medical School. As soon as he saw me, tears welled up in his eyes. He looked at me a moment, and then exclaimed: "I say, old fellow, you are alive! What a pleasant surprise. How are you getting along?"

Without waiting for an answer, he continued: "Last night, we heard that Hiroshima had been attacked by a new weapon. The damage was slight, they told us, but in order to see for myself and to lend a hand if extra physicians were needed, I secured a truck and came on down. What a frightful mess greeted us when we arrived. Are you sure *you* are all right?"

And again, without stopping for me to reply, he went on to tell about the heartbreaking things he witnessed from the truck as he entered the city. These were the first details any of us had heard, so we listened intently.

While he talked, all I could think of was the fear and uncertainty that must be preying on my old mother who lived in the country near Okayama. When he had finished, I asked Dr. Nishimura if he would get word to my mother, and also to a sister who lived in Okayama, that Yaeko-san and I were safe. He assured me that he would, and before leaving he also promised to organize a team of doctors and nurses to come down and help as soon as he could get them together.

Dr. Tabuchi, an old friend from Ushita, came in. His face and hands had been burned, though not badly, and after an exchange of greetings, I asked if he knew what had happened.

"I was in the back yard pruning some trees when it exploded," he answered. "The first thing I knew, there was a blinding white flash of light, and a wave of intense heat struck my cheek. This was odd, I thought, when in the next instant there was a tremendous blast.

"The force of it knocked me clean over," he continued, "but fortunately, it didn't hurt me; and my wife wasn't hurt either. But you should have seen our house! It didn't topple over, it just inclined. I have never seen such a mess. Inside and out everything was simply ruined. Even so, we are happy to be alive, and what's more Ryoji, our son, survived. I didn't tell you that he had gone into the city on business that morning. About midnight, after we had given up all hope that he could possibly survive in the dreadful fire that followed the blast, he came home. Listen!" he continued, "why don't you come on home with me? My house is certainly nothing to look at now, but it is better than here."

It was impossible for me to accept his kind offer, and I tried to decline in a way that would not hurt his feelings.

"Dr. Tabuchi," I replied, "we are all grateful for your kind offer, but Dr. Katsube has just warned me that I must lie perfectly still until my wounds are healed."

Dr. Tabuchi accepted my explanation with some reluctance, and after a pause he made ready to go.

"Don't go," I said. "Please tell us more of what occurred yesterday."

"It was a horrible sight," said Dr. Tabuchi. "Hundreds of injured people who were trying to escape to the hills passed our house. The sight of them was almost unbearable. Their faces and hands were burnt and swollen; and great sheets of skin had peeled away from their tissues to hang down like rags on a scarecrow. They moved like a line of ants. All through the night, they went past our house, but this morning they had stopped. I found them lying on both sides of the road so thick that it was impossible to pass without stepping on them."

I lay with my eyes shut while Dr. Tabuchi was talking, picturing in my mind the horror he was describing. I neither saw nor heard Mr. Katsutani when he came in. It was not until I heard someone sobbing that my attention was attracted, and I recognized my old friend. I had known Mr. Katsutani for many years and knew him to be an emotional person, but even so, to see him break down made tears come to my eyes. He had come all the way from Jigozen to look for me, and now that he had found me, emotion overcame him.

He turned to Dr. Sasada and said brokenly: "Yesterday, it was impossible to enter Hiroshima, else I would have come. Even today fires are still burning in some places. You should see how the city has changed. When I reached the Misasa Bridge this morning, everything before me was gone, even the castle. These buildings here are the only ones left anywhere around. The Communications Bureau seemed to loom right in front of me long before I got anywhere near here."

Mr. Katsutani paused for a moment to catch his breath and went on: "I *really* walked along the railroad tracks to get here, but even they were littered with electric wires and broken railway cars, and the dead and wounded lay everywhere. When I reached the bridge, I saw a dreadful thing. It was unbelievable. There was a man, stone dead, sitting on his bicycle as it leaned against the bridge railing. It is hard to believe that such a thing could happen!"

He repeated himself two or three times as if to convince himself that what he said was true and then continued: "It seems that most of the dead people were either on the bridge or beneath it. You could tell that many had gone down to the river to get a drink of water and had died where they lay. I saw a few live people still in the water, knocking against the dead as they floated down the river. There must have been hundreds and thousands who fled to the river to escape the fire and then drowned.

"The sight of the soldiers, though, was more dreadful than the dead people floating down the river. I came onto I don't know how many, burned from the hips up; and where the skin had peeled, their flesh was wet and mushy. They must have been wearing their military caps because the black hair on top of their heads was not burned. It made them look like they were wearing black lacquer bowls.

"And they had no faces! Their eyes, noses and mouths had been burned away, and it looked like their ears had melted off. It was hard to tell front from back. One soldier, whose features had been destroyed and was left with his white teeth sticking out, asked me for some water, but I didn't have any. I clasped my hands and prayed for him. He didn't say anything more. His plea for water must have been his last words. The way they were burned, I wonder if they didn't have their coats off when the bomb exploded."

It seemed to give Mr. Katsutani some relief to pour out his terrifying experiences on us; and there was no one who would have stopped him, so fascinating was his tale of horror. While he was talking, several people came in and stayed to listen. Somebody asked him what he was doing when the explosion occurred.

"I had just finished breakfast," he replied, "and was getting ready to light a cigarette, when all of a sudden I saw a white flash. In a moment there was a tremendous blast. Not stopping to think, I let out a yell and jumped into an air-raid dugout. In a moment there was such a blast as I have never heard before. It was terrific! I jumped out of the dugout and pushed my wife into it. Realizing something terrible must have happened in Hiroshima, I climbed up onto the roof of my storehouse to have a look."

Mr. Katsutani became more intense and, gesticulating wildly, went on: "Towards Hiroshima, I saw a big black cloud go billowing up, like a puffy summer cloud. Knowing for sure then that something terrible had happened in the city, I jumped down from my storehouse and ran as fast as I could to the military post at Hatsukaichi. I ran up to the officer in charge and told him what I had seen and begged him to send sombody to help in Hiroshima. But he didn't even take me seriously. He looked at me for a moment with a threatening expression, and then do you know what he said? He said, 'There isn't much to worry about. One or two bombs won't hurt Hiroshima.' There was no use talking to that fool!

"I was the ranking officer in the local branch of the Ex-officer's Association, but even I didn't know what to do because that day the villagers under my command had been sent off to Miyajima for labor service. I looked all around to find someone to help me make a rescue squad, but I couldn't find anybody. While I was still looking for help, wounded people began to stream into the village. I asked them what had happened, but all they could tell me was that Hiroshima had been destroyed and everybody was leaving the city. With that I got on my bicycle and rode as fast as I could towards Itsukaichi. By the time I got there, the road was jammed with people, and so was every path and byway.

"Again I tried to find out what had happened, but nobody could give me a clear answer. When I asked these people where they had come from, they would point towards Hiroshima and say, 'This way.' And when I asked where they were going, they would point toward Miyajima and say, 'That way.' Everybody said the same thing.

"I saw no badly wounded or burned people around Itsukaichi, but when I reached Kusatsu, nearly everybody was badly hurt. The nearer I got to Hiroshima the more I saw until by the time I had reached Koi, they were all so badly injured, I could not bear to look into their faces. They smelled like burning hair."

Mr. Katsutani paused for a moment to take a deep breath and then continued: "The area around Koi station was not burned, but the station and the houses nearby were badly damaged. Every square inch of the station platform was packed with wounded people. Some were standing; others lying down. They were all pleading for water. Now and then you could hear a child calling for its mother. It was a living hell, I tell you. It was a living hell!

"Today it was the same way.

"Did Dr. Hanaoka come to the hospital yesterday? I saw him cross the streetcar trestle at Koi and head in this direction, but I can't believe that he could have made his way through that fire."

"No, we haven't seen him," someone answered.

Mr. Katsutani nodded reflectively and went on: "I left Koi station and went over to the Koi primary school. By then, the school had been turned into an emergency hospital and was already crowded with desperately injured people. Even the playground was packed with the dead and dying. They looked like so many codfish spread out for drying. What a pitiful sight it was to see them lying there in the hot sun. Even I could tell they were all going to die.

"Towards evening, I was making my way back to the highway when I ran into my sister. My sister, whose home had been in Tokaichi, must surely have been killed. But here she was—alive! She was so happy, she couldn't utter a word! All she could do was cry. If ever anyone shed tears of joy, she did. Some kind people lent me a hand in making a stretcher and helped carry her back to my home in Jigozen near Miyajima Guchi. Even my little village, as far re-moved as it was from Hiroshima, had become a living hell. Every shrine, every temple was packed and jammed with wounded people."

Mr. Katsutani had said all he had in him to say. He left our room, but instead of going home, he stayed to help with the wounded.

The stories of Dr. Nishimura, Dr. Tabuchi, and Mr. Katsutani left no doubt in my mind about the destruction of Hiroshima. I had seen enough to know that the damage was heavy, but what they had told me was unbelievable.

When I thought of the injured, lying in the sun begging for water, I felt as though I were committing a sin by being where I was. I no longer felt quite so sorry for those of our patients who were obliged to lie on the hard concrete floors in the toilets.

My thoughts turned to myself.

"If only I hadn't been hurt," I mused, "I could be doing something instead of lying here as a patient, requiring the attention of my comrades. Wounded and helpless. What a plight, when all about me there is so much to do!"

Fortunately, my dismal thoughts were interrupted. Who should make an appearance but Dr. Hanaoka, our internist, whom Mr. Katsutani had just told us was last seen at Hatsukaichi.

"Dr. Hachiya, you don't know how happy I am to see you!" exclaimed Dr. Hanaoka. "After seeing what has happened to Hiroshima, it's a miracle anyone survived."

"We have been worrying about you, Dr. Hanaoka," I replied, "because Mr. Katsutani told us only a few minutes ago that he saw you disappear in the direction

of Hiroshima while he was at the Koi station yesterday. Where have you been, and how did you get here?"

"Now that I'm here, I wonder myself," said Dr.
Hanaoka. "Let me tell you, if I can, what happened.
Somebody told me that a special, new bomb was
dropped near the Gokoku Shrine. If what I was told is
true, then that bomb must have had terrific power,
for from the Gokoku Shrine clean out to the Red Cross
Hospital [a mile away] everything is completely destroyed. The Red Cross Hospital, though badly damaged, was spared, and beyond, going towards Ujina
the damage is slight.

"I stopped by the Red Cross Hospital on my way
here. It is swamped with patients, and outside the dead
and dying are lined up on either side of the street as
far east as the Miyuki Bridge.

"Between the Red Cross Hospital and the center of
the city I saw nothing that wasn't burned to a crisp.
Streetcars were standing at Kawaya-cho and Kamiya-
cho and inside were dozens of bodies, blackened beyond recognition. I saw fire reservoirs filled to the
brim with dead people who looked as though they had
been boiled alive. In one reservoir I saw a man, horribly burned, crouching beside another man who was
dead. He was drinking blood-stained water out of
the reservoir. Even if I had tried to stop him, it
wouldn't have done any good; he was completely out
of his head. In one reservoir there were so many dead
people there wasn't enough room for them to fall over.
They must have died sitting in the water.

"Even the swimming pool at the Prefectural First
Middle School is filled with dead people. They must

have suffocated while they sat in the water trying to escape the fire because they didn't appear to be burned."

Dr. Hanaoka cleared his throat, and after a moment continued: "Dr. Hachiya, that pool wasn't big enough to accommodate everybody who tried to get in it. You could tell that by looking around the sides. I don't know how many were caught by death with their heads hanging over the edge. In one pool I saw some people who were still alive, sitting in the water with dead all around them. They were too weak to get out. People were trying to help them, but I am sure they must have died. I apologize for telling you these things, but they are true. I don't see how anyone got out alive."

Dr. Hanaoka paused, and I could see he was anxious to get to work. With what there was to do, it would have been criminal to detain him.

Gradually, what these visitors were telling me began to fit into a pattern. A few comments from this one, a few remarks from another, were beginning to give me a picture of what Hiroshima was like.

Dr. Hanaoka had barely left when Dr. Akiyama, head of obstetrics and gynecology, came in. He was unhurt but looked tired and worn.

"Sit down and rest a few minutes," I said. "You must have been through a great deal. Where were you when the bombing occurred?"

"I was just leaving my home when it went off," said Dr. Akiyama in a tremulous voice. "A blinding flash, a tremendous explosion, and over I went on my back. And then a big black cloud, such as you see in the summer before a storm, began to rise above Hiroshima. '*Yarareta*,' I shouted; and that was it. What a hodge-podge was made of my house. The ceilings, the walls, the sliding doors—everything—ruined beyond repair.

"Almost at once, injured people began to line up before my gate, and from then until a little while ago, I stayed and treated them. But my supplies are all gone, and there is nothing left to treat them with. Twenty or thirty people are still lying in the house and there is nobody to take care of them. There is nothing anybody can do, unless I find some more supplies."

Dr. Akiyama, ordinarily easygoing and happy, had the look of a man distraught. Dr. Koyama came in while Dr. Akiyama was talking and so heard most of what he had been saying.

"Knowing you, I can imagine what you have gone through," said Dr. Koyama.

"I don't know," sighed Dr. Akiyama. "Today it's the same as it was yesterday. There is no end to that stream of miserable souls who stop at my house to ask for help. They are trying to reach Kabe, but they will never get there. And there is nothing I can do; nothing anybody can do."

Since Dr. Akiyama's home was in Nagatsuka, I got a general idea of what that suburb was like. The problem there was the same as in the Koi area. I could picture in my mind the wounded people walking in silence, like lost spirits, and answering, when questioned, that they had come "this way" and were going "that way." I could see them begging for water, hear their moaning, and see them dying. I might have been there myself, so vividly had my friends recounted to me what they had seen.

It was reported that none of the patients had any appetite and that one by one they were beginning to vomit and have diarrhea. Did the new weapon I had heard about throw off a poison gas or perhaps some deadly germ? I asked Dr. Hanaoka to confirm if he could the report of vomiting and diarrhea and to find out if any of the patients looked as if they might have an infectious disease. He inquired and brought word that there were many who not only had diarrhea but bloody stools and that some had had as many as forty to fifty stools during the previous night. This convinced me that we were dealing with bacillary dysentery and had no choice but to isolate those who were infected.

Dr. Koyama, as deputy director, was given the responsibility of setting up an isolation ward. He chose a site on the grounds beyond the south side of the hospital, and with the help of some soldiers who happened along he managed to construct what amounted to a crude outdoor pavillion. What we were trying to do probably was not worth much, but it helped our morale to think we were doing something.

Dr. Katsube and his staff had an impossible task. There was scarcely a patient who was not in need of urgent surgical care. The doctors and nurses were all busy helping him. Even the clerical staff and janitors, and those among the patients who could so much as get about, were organized and instructed to help. If progress was made, it was hard to see. How Dr. Katsube did what he did was a miracle.

The corridors were cleared enough to be passable, but in a little while they were as crowded as before. One difficulty was the influx of people looking for friends and relatives.

Parents, half crazy with grief, searched for their children. Husbands looked for their wives, and children for their parents. One poor woman, insane with anxiety, walked aimlessly here and there through the hospital calling her child's name. It was dreadfully upsetting to patients, but no one had the heart to stop her. Another woman stood at the entrance, shouting mournfully for someone she thought was inside. She, too, upset us.

Not a few came in from the country to look for friends or relatives. They would wander among the patients and peer rudely into every face, until finally their behavior became so intolerable that we had to refuse them entrance to the hospital.

A new noise reached us from outside. On inquiry, I was told that Dr. Koyama had procured a company of soldiers to clean out the fire-damaged Communications Bureau, so that it could be put in use again as an annex to the hospital.

The pharmacy came to life. Our meager supply of drugs was sorted and prepared for use under the watchful supervision of Dr. Hinoi and Mr. Mizoguchi.

A little order was appearing; something positive was being done. Perhaps in time we could get control of the situation.

Mr. Sera, the business manager, reported. He told me that sixteen patients had died during the night and that he had shrouded their bodies in white blankets and deposited them at the side entrance to the hospital.

"Can we spare those blankets at a time like this?" I thought to myself.

I was reluctant to object openly to what Mr. Sera had done because his action had been prompted by his sense of propriety and respect for the dead. When I discovered, however, that the army detail, dispatched to remove the dead, had thrown the bodies, blankets and all, onto the platform of a truck without any ceremony whatsoever, I seized on this indignity to suggest that our blankets be saved. The living needed the blankets more than the dead.

Patients continued to come from all directions, and since we were not far removed from the center of the explosion, those who came were in a critical condition.

Their behavior was remarkable. Even though the ones in the hospital fared little better than those on the outside, they were grateful for a pallet in the most crowded ward. It seemed to satisfy them if they could get so much as a glimpse of a white-robed doctor or nurse. A kind word was enough to set them crying. For the most trivial service they would clasp their hands and pray for you. All were sufferers together and were confident that the doctors and nurses would do their best for them. Later, word came that this hospital was considered a good place to be in. The remark pleased us, but we were never able to feel that we had done as much as we should.

Earlier in the day Mr. Imachi and those who worked with him in the kitchen managed to prepare some rice gruel which they brought in by the bucketful and dished out with big wooden spoons. For me, this simple gruel made the one bright spot in the day. It was served again that afternoon, and the mouthful I had, and the grain of rice that remained on my tongue, made me feel that I was going to get well. But there were many who were too weak or too sick to eat. In time, the weakness of hunger added to their misery.

Night approached and still the only beds were straw mats laid over the concrete floor. Wounds were becoming more painful, and there were not enough drugs to make them easy. Fevers rose and the patients became thirsty, but there was no one to bring cool water to quench the thirst.

Dr. Harada, one of our pharmacists, was brought into the hospital severely burned, and right after him, old Mrs. Saeki's son in the same condition. Miss Hinada, one of our nurses, had to be confined because of a severe diarrhea that had begun earlier in the day. Since there was no one to nurse her, her mother, despite being seriously burned, was trying to do the job.

Mr. Mizoguchi came in: "Dr. Hachiya, I must tell you that Miss Hinada and her mother have become worse. It doesn't look like either of them will live through the night, and old Mrs. Saeki's son is losing consciousness."

All day I had listened to visitors telling me about the destruction of Hiroshima and the scenes of horror

they had witnessed. I had seen my friends wounded,
their families separated, their homes destroyed. I was
aware of the problems our staff had to face, and I knew
how bravely they struggled against superhuman odds.
I knew what the patients had to endure and the trust
they put in the doctors and nurses, who, could they
know the truth, were as helpless as themselves.

By degrees my capacity to comprehend the magni-
tude of their sorrow, to share with them the pain, frus-
tration, and horror became so dulled that I found myself accepting whatever was told me with equanimity
and a detachment I would never have believed possible.

In two days I had become at home in this environment of chaos and despair.

I felt lonely, but it was an animal loneliness. I became part of the darkness of the night. There were no
radios, no electric lights, not even a candle. The only
light that came to me was reflected in flickering shadows made by the burning city. The only sounds were
the groans and sobs of the patients. Now and then a
patient in delirium would call for his mother, or the
voice of one in pain would breathe out the word *eraiyo*
—"the pain is unbearable; I cannot endure it!"

What kind of a bomb was it that had destroyed Hiroshima? What had my visitors told me earlier? Whatever it was, it did not make sense.

There could not have been more than a few planes.
Even *my* memory would agree to that. Before the air-
raid alarm there was the metallic sound of one plane
and no more. Otherwise why did the alarm stop? Why

was there no further alarm during the five or six minutes before the explosion occurred?

Reason as I would, I could not make the ends meet when I considered the destruction that followed. Perhaps it *was* a new weapon! More than one of my visitors spoke vaguely of a "new bomb," a "secret weapon," a "special bomb," and someone even said that the bomb was suspended from two parachutes when it burst! Whatever it was, it was beyond my comprehension. Damage of this order could have no explanation! All we had were stories no more substantial than the clouds from which we had reached to snatch them.

One thing was certain—Hiroshima was destroyed; and with it the army that had been quartered in Hiroshima. Gone were headquarters, gone the command post of the Second General Army and the Military School for young people, the General Headquarters for the Western Command, the Corps of Engineers, and the Army Hospital. Gone was the hope of Japan! The war was lost! No more help would come from the gods!

American forces would soon be landing; and when they landed, there would be street fighting; and our hospital would become a place of attack and defense. Had I not heard earlier that soldiers were coming to set up headquarters in the Communications Bureau? Would we be turned out?

Were there no answers?

Dr. Sasada, Miss Kado, and my wife were asleep. That was good, but there was no sleep for me.

I heard footsteps, and a man appeared at the door, outlined in the flickering darkness. His elbows were out and his hands down, like the burned people I had seen on my way to the hospital. As he came nearer, I could see his face—or what had been his face because this face had been melted away by the fire. The man was blind and had lost his way.

"You are in the wrong room!" I shouted, suddenly stricken with terror.

The poor fellow turned and shuffled back into the night. I was ashamed for having behaved as I did, but I was frightened. Now more awake than ever, every nerve taut, I could find no sleep.

To the east there was a perceptible lightening of the sky.

My shouting must have wakened my wife because she got up and left the room, I suppose to find the toilet. Before long she was back.

"What is the matter, Yaeko-san?" I asked, sensing she was upset.

"*O-tōsan*, the hall was so full of patients that I could find nowhere to walk without disturbing someone," she answered, trying to suppress her agitation. "I had to excuse myself every step I took. Oh! it was terrible. Finally, I stepped on somebody's foot, and when I asked to be excused, there was no answer. I looked down; and do you know what I had done?"

"What?" I asked.

"I had stepped on a dead man's foot," she said and with a shudder moved nearer.

8 August 1945

The day began hot and clear. The sun was hardly up before my body was moist with oily sweat that dripped from my armpits and the inner sides of my thighs.

Smoke no longer rose from the second floor.

Dr. Sasada's face was more swollen this morning than yesterday, and blood-stained pus oozed from his bandaged arms and hands. I felt a wave of pity when I thought how he had used those hands to help me two days ago.

A noise outside the window caused me to recall a patient I neglected to mention yesterday. From time to time during the night I had heard him walking about, and this morning, he was walking again. You could hear him especially well when he stumbled into the fence or against the building.

"Has he been fed?" I asked Miss Kado.

"Don't worry, Doctor," replied Miss Kado. "There are plenty of potato leaves in the garden, so I don't think he'll be hungry."

The patient we were talking about was a horse who had been burned and blinded by the fire. Whoever saw him first did not have the heart to turn him away, so he was put in the garden under our window.

This garden had been a tennis court, but some time ago I thought it could be better used as a garden and I planted it in potatoes. My try at gardening caused

no little amusement, and my potatoes came to be a
joke.

"Miss Kado," I asked, "don't you think we had better dig up the potatoes? They must be quite big by
now."

My companions laughed, and for a moment misery
was forgotten.

My left ankle began to hurt. Looking down, I discovered that it had become wet and sticky through the
bandage. Miss Kado saw my concern and offered to
change the dressing, and when she finished, the ankle
felt better. While she was changing the dressing
though, I noticed a big blister on my left knee. This
was a surprise because I could not recollect having
received any burns. Later I remembered the hot ember that struck my leg while I was lying in the garden behind the Communications Bureau.

My appetite was better this morning and I seemed
to be stronger. Even my spirits were improved, and the
dark thoughts that had beset me during the night were
less oppressive.

Dr. Katsube came early. Instead of greeting him with
a good morning, I asked him point-blank when I could
get up. He told me again that it would be at least a
week before he could remove the stitches and that I
was to say no more about getting up until then.

"You are too impatient," he said. "You should be
thankful that you are going to live."

That I might die had never crossed my mind, but
now that Dr. Katsube had spoken so bluntly, I realized
that I must have been hurt worse than I thought.

"Was I that bad off?" I asked, trying to appear nonchalant.

"We were worried about you," Dr. Katsube stated. "Perhaps you don't realize how much blood you lost. Why, you remained comatose for the better part of the night! Your wife, Miss Kado, and Dr. Sasada, as well as Dr. Koyama and I, were, one or the other of us, at your side all night."

"No wonder I remember so little of what happened that night," I replied, trying to pass off his comments lightly.

I should have been content to rest. Dr. Koyama was certainly doing a good job of running the hospital, and I was in touch with things. Not only did he keep me informed, but he referred matters to me for opinion where he might have acted without doing me that courtesy.

A note, for example, came from Dr. Chodo, one of our dentists, which stated that he and his family were hiding in the hills behind Ushita. His family was unhurt, but he had been badly burned and asked if someone could bring him to the hospital. I sent for him, in spite of our critical shortage at the hospital.

Another report informed us that the Welfare Department of the Communications Bureau had between two hundred and three hundred sleeping mats, or *tatami*, which could be procured for use in the hospital. Since these mats were roughly three by six feet in dimensions, the question arose, since we were so crowded, how we could get them under the patients. Mr. Sera and I felt that, crowded or not, the sleeping mats must be used, even if it meant clearing all the corridors.

A rumor that Mr. Yoshida, chief of the Communications Bureau, had been killed proved to be true. His charred body, identified by a belt buckle, was found near the hospital, and his remains were cremated in front of the Communications Bureau. In his death we lost a kind and loyal friend. Another prominent person to be killed was Mayor Otsuka.

I was startled to learn that I had been reported killed. The news was brought by two old friends, Mr. and Mrs. Nagao of Nishihara, who came looking for Yaeko-san and me this morning. We were happy to disprove the report of my death.

During the day, an effort was made to sort and rearrange the patients according to the nature and severity of their injuries, and not a few dead were found among the living, though fewer than yesterday. It irritated me when I heard the report, for I felt that the dead should be moved with greater dispatch in order to make room for the living. This is another example of my changed outlook. People were dying so fast that I had begun to accept death as a matter of course and ceased to respect its awfulness. I considered a family lucky if it had not lost more than two of its members. How could I hold my head up among the citizens of Hiroshima with thoughts like that in my mind?

Soldiers began to work again in the Communications Bureau. Dr. Koyama and I discussed the feasibility of getting them to help clear one of the floors for the patients quartered in the toilets and corridors. While we were talking, Dr. Hanaoka informed us that bloody diarrhea was increasing and that some had had as many as sixty stools since daybreak.

For the moment, a hospital annex in the Communications Bureau seemed less urgently needed than an enlarged isolation ward, so the soldiers were asked to help with the latter. [It was perfectly logical to assume that the outbreak of bloody diarrhea represented the beginning of a dysentery epidemic and that the only possible way to control its spread would be to isolate the patients thus afflicted. The doctors in Hiroshima did not know that an atom bomb had been dropped, much less the fact that bloody diarrhea was a symptom of serious radiation sickness.—*Translator's note.*]

The problem of how to reutilize the hospital came up for discussion because the fire-damaged second story had cooled down enough to be used. Before the fire there had been fourteen rooms above us, but since all the partitions were now destroyed, nothing remained but one single large room.

The question as to who among the patients should be moved upstairs provoked lively debate since it seemed at the time that the burned-out second floor was far less desirable than the first, despite the crowding. It was finally decided that we, as staff members, should be the first to go up and leave the more desirable ground floor for patients from the outside.

I was moved first, and when my stretcher cleared the landing, my inquiring eyes fixed on the stark and twisted remains of thirty-odd iron bed frames, under each of which lay a white ash residue of the straw mattresses that had once covered them. There was not a sound bed frame on the floor, but after two days spent lying on the concrete floor, the very sight of these beds was magnificent. Yaeko-san and I found beds near each other that were not too badly bent. Our sleeping mats were placed over the frames, and without further ado we were ready to resume life in our new quarters.

Dr. Sasada, Miss Susukida, and Miss Omoto joined us, and one by one other members of the staff were brought up until the big room became alive with people. One might have complained about the soot and ashes or about the pipes and curtain rods that hung crazily from the ceiling, but patients never lived in a hospital ward so nearly free of bacteria as this one that was sterilized by fire.

In all four walls were large casement windows which afforded a commanding view in every direction. There were no shutters, no curtains, nor even glass to impose the least obstruction to air or light. Looking east, south, and west, was an unobstructed view of Hiroshima and in Hiroshima Bay we could see the island Ninoshima.

Near the center of the city, some fifteen hundred meters distant, one could see the blackened ruins of the two largest buildings in Hiroshima, the Fukuya Department Store and the Chūgoku Press Building. Hijiyama, the sacred and beautiful little mountain in the eastern sector of the city, looked almost close enough to touch. To our north no buildings remained.

For the first time, I could understand what my friends had meant when they said Hiroshima was destroyed. Nothing remained except a few buildings of reinforced concrete, two of which I just mentioned. For acres and acres the city was like a desert except for scattered piles of brick and roof tile. I had to revise my meaning of the word destruction or choose some other word to describe what I saw. Devastation may be a better word, but really, I know of no word or words to describe the view from my twisted iron bed in the fire-gutted ward of the Communications Hospital.

I could see the soldiers working on our isolation ward. One took the lead in a work song and the others answered in chorus, verse for verse. In no time a forty-square-yard addition to the ward was completed. Behind this they constructed an outdoor toilet with partitions of straw mats. From where I lay the mats provided no concealment.

A gentle breeze blew through the windows, bringing relief to our fevered bodies. Gone were the confusion and disorder we had known downstairs. The abundant light from wide open windows and the distant vistas did something to our spirits. The very simplicity of our surroundings, contrasted with the chaos below, had a soothing effect.

We thought we had left the better part of the hospital for the patients downstairs, but now that we had moved in all agreed that ours were the better quarters. I resolved to have this room made available to the others as soon as possible.

Towards evening, a light southerly wind blowing across the city wafted to us an odor suggestive of burning sardines. I wondered what could cause such a smell until somebody, noticing it too, informed me that sanitation teams were cremating the remains of people who had been killed. Looking out, I could discern numerous fires scattered about the city. Previously I had assumed the fires were caused by burning rubble. Towards Nigitsu was an especially large fire where the dead were being burned by hundreds. To realize suddenly that these fires were funeral pyres made me shudder, and I became a little nauseated.

Concrete buildings near the center of the city, still afire on the inside, made eerie silhouettes against the night sky. These glowing ruins and the blazing funeral pyres set me to wondering if Pompeii had not looked like this during its last days. But I think there were not so many dead in Pompeii as there were in Hiroshima.

For nearly three days the hospital staff had been laboring with scarcely a break, so tonight in order to give them a little respite, a space was cleared in our upstairs ward and alternate shifts were ordered to rest.

Dr. Koyama stopped to talk a few minutes before lying down and told me some of the things that had happened during the day.

In the morning a group of soldiers had come to the entrance, demanding bandages for the Second General Army, and despite the staff's assertion that our materials were low, made away with nearly all we had. These men behaved more like brigands than soldiers. Moreover, what they did was contrary to what we had been told to expect, because the army had repeatedly promised to supply us with emergency goods in case of attack. These soldiers could not have come from the army that had been stationed in Hiroshima. There were not enough soldiers left in that group to help with the wounded soldiers brought to the hospital. The army was unable to provide for the wounded family of the local commandant whom we had made room for in one of the toilets. When the commandant's adjutant found them, he could find no better place to take them and was grateful when we managed to squeeze them into the janitor's office. The soldiers who got our supplies must have come from somewhere else.

We had further cause to worry. Dr. Koyama told me that soldiers from somewhere had been around all day cleaning out the Communications Bureau, and that rumors were current that an army headquarters was to be set up to direct a defense of Hiroshima in case of invasion. We both agreed that if an army should move in, our hospital would become a target for more bombing, and next time we would all be killed.

After Dr. Koyama left I continued to think along these lines, became upset, and could not sleep. I could hear every little sigh during the night, every plea for water, every groan. One of the dysentery patients who had been transferred to the isolation ward went to the back of the Bureau to get a drink of water. I heard a rude man scold him and tell him to go away lest he pass his dysentery on to him.

One voice called repeatedly for water, and as the night wore on the voice became weaker. I asked a nurse who the patient was, and she told me that he was a young officer who appeared to be from a decent family because every time she gave him a drink of water he thanked her politely.

Mention of the young officer called to mind a visit Yaeko-san and I had had on the second of August. A cousin, Captain Urabe, and his wife spent the day with us. Captain Urabe had been recruited as an army doctor shortly after he graduated from medical school, and when I saw him he had been eating army food for six or seven years in northern and central China. To me he appeared well-disciplined and courageous.

I was pessimistic about the outcome of the war and told him so. I confided that I thought we were going to lose because everything was becoming scarce, and the soldiers were no longer disciplined. I said that I was afraid Hiroshima was going to be bombed and that if it were the antiaircraft guns would be useless. Our defenses had been prepared for incendiary bombing, and I considered it nonsensical to think the enemy would use incendiary bombs on a city with as many rivers and vacant lots as there were in Hiroshima.

To this my cousin listened calmly, and then replied: "*Niisan,* don't you worry for a minute. The chief of staff has said that no matter how much the nation criticizes the army, the army will reply with victory!"

As I lay there in the dark, I mumbled to myself, "Reply with victory." Where was my cousin now? If I could find him, he might be able to get us the medical supplies we needed. Captain Urabe must be busy, otherwise he would have come to see me before now.

9 August 1945

The day began hot and clear, but upstairs the sun did not shine directly on us as it had downstairs. In addition, a cool breeze that blew right across the ward helped make our situation altogether more agreeable than it had been yesterday.

My mouth was more comfortable this morning so the healing of my lip and cheek must be progressing satisfactorily. Indeed, I felt so much better that I asked if I might have some rice to eat instead of rice gruel. Miss Kado, always thoughtful, dug some of the sweet potatoes I had planted and prepared them for me. I do not think sweet potatoes ever tasted so good.

My wife, although still with her arm in a sling, was so much better this morning that she took care of me. I was amused to hear her ask for some white ointment which she put over her brows to conceal the fact that her eyebrows had been singed. Her returning vanity was a good sign.

Dr. Sasada was worse this morning. His temperature had increased, and he was weaker.

The sun had not been up long before visitors again appeared. One of the most welcome was a sturdy soldier, who staggered in under a load of bandages and drugs much too large for one person to carry. He had been sent by Lieutenant Tanaka of the Akatsuki Corps. Not only was I pleased to receive the badly needed medical supplies, but it was good to learn that Lieutenant Tanaka was alive. I had known this young officer through my cousin, Captain Urabe. His thoughtfulness was gratefully acknowledged by everyone.

There was another surprise. His excellency, Mr. Okamoto, head of the Western District of the Communications Ministry, came to see me. I had heard a good deal about him, naturally, but had not had an opportunity to meet him. He was a sociable, friendly man who immediately put me at ease. When we discovered by coincidence that I had followed him by six

years in the same high school in Okayama, all barriers
of authority disappeared, and we fell to talking of old
times. He was on the way to Hiroshima when the
bombing occurred and would have been here at the
time had he not been stung by a bee near Kure, a city
twenty-five miles south of Hiroshima, with the result
that he stopped off for treatment. That bee saved his
life.

During conversation with Mr. Okamoto, I sat up
without thinking, from deference to my distinguished
visitor. After he left, I suddenly realized that it had not
hurt to sit up. If I could sit without pain, could I not
stand? I waited until no one was looking and tried,
but the stitches in my hip began to pull; so somewhat
crestfallen, I was obliged to lie down. Nevertheless,
this experiment inspired me with confidence. Once
my stitches were out, I was convinced I could be active
again.

Today, Dr. Hanaoka's report on the patients was
more detailed. One observation particularly impressed me. Regardless of the type of injury, nearly
everybody had the same symptoms. All had a poor
appetite, the majority had nausea and gaseous indi-
gestion, and over half had vomiting.

Not a few had shown improvement since yesterday.
Diarrhea, though, continued to be a problem and actually appeared to be increasing. Distinctly alarming
was the appearance of blood in the stools of patients
who earlier had only diarrhea. The isolation of these
people was becoming increasingly difficult.

One seriously ill man complained of a sore mouth
yesterday, and today, numerous small hemorrhages be-

gan to appear in his mouth and under his skin. His case was the more puzzling because he came to the hospital complaining of weakness and nausea and did not appear to have been injured at all.

This morning, other patients were beginning to show small subcutaneous hemorrhages, and not a few were coughing and vomiting blood in addition to passing it in their stools. One poor woman was bleeding from her privates. Among these patients there was not one with symptoms typical of anything we knew, unless you could exclude those who developed signs of severe brain disease before they died.

Dr. Hanaoka believed the patients could be divided into three groups:

1. Those with nausea, vomiting, and diarrhea who were improving.

2. Those with nausea, vomiting, and diarrhea who were remaining stationary.

3. Those with nausea, vomiting, and diarrhea who were developing hemorrhage under the skin or elsewhere.

Had these patients been burned or otherwise injured, we might have tried to stretch the logic of cause and effect and assume that their bizarre symptoms were related to injury, but so many patients appeared to have received no injury whatsoever that we were obliged to postulate an assault heretofore unknown.

The only other possible cause for the weird symptoms observed was a sudden change in atmospheric pressure. I had read somewhere about bleeding that follows ascent to high altitudes and about bleeding in deep sea divers who ascend too rapidly from the depths.

Having never seen such injury I could not give much credence to my thoughts.

Still, it was impossible to dismiss the thought that atmospheric pressure had had something to do with the symptoms of our patients. During my student days at Okayama University, I had seen experiments conducted in a pressure chamber. Sudden, temporary deafness was one symptom everyone complained of if pressure in the chamber was abruptly altered.

Now, I could state positively that I had heard nothing like an explosion when we were bombed the other morning, nor did I remember any sound during my walk to the hospital as houses collapsed around me. It was as though I walked through a gloomy, silent motion picture. Others whom I questioned had had the same experience.

Those who experienced the bombing from the outskirts of the city characterized it by the word: *pikadon* [flash-boom!].

How then could one account for my failure and the failure of others to hear an explosion except on the premise that a sudden change in atmospheric pressure had rendered those nearby temporarily deaf. Could the bleeding we were beginning to observe be explained on the same basis?

Since all books and journals had been destroyed, there was no way to corroborate my theories except by further appeal to the patients. To that end Dr. Katsube was asked to discover what else he could when he made ward rounds.

It was pleasing to note my scientific curiosity was reviving, and I lost no opportunity to question everyone who visited me about the bombing of Hiroshima. Their answers were vague and ambiguous, and on one point only were they in agreement: a new weapon had been used. *What* the new weapon was became a burning question. Not only had our books been destroyed, but our newspapers, telephones, and radios as well.

Dr. Chodo, our dentist, whom I spoke of earlier as having fled with his family to the Ushita hills, was brought in and assigned with his family to the waiting room of the Dental Department. I asked the nurse who helped bring him in how he was.

"Dr. Chodo is in a serious condition," she told me. "It is frightful to see all of him burned and glistening with oozing secretions. I don't believe he will live."

"How about his wife and daughter?" I asked.

"They weren't hurt," answered the nurse.

Poor Dr. Chodo. He and his family only recently came up from Okinawa and had no relatives here and few friends. What would happen to his family if he died?

While I lay there brooding over Dr. Chodo, old Mrs. Saeki came up quietly and stood by my bed. One look into her pale, careworn face and I knew what she had come to say. Her son was dead; her eldest son—her only child left in the world. She had been so hopeful yesterday when he was brought in, and now he was gone. Her son's wife and her second son had been killed on the day of the *pikadon,* and now no one was left. She put her hands over her eyes and cried, but her sobs were scarcely audible. I could not speak for a while because there was something in my throat.

"Obāsan," I said when I could control my voice, "don't worry. I will look after you hereafter."

Old Mrs. Saeki stood for a while, crying quietly. Then she said: "Please help me, Doctor," and without saying anything more, turned and went downstairs.

My thoughts returned to Dr. Harada. Except for the top of his head, every inch was burned, leaving his pus-glistening body red and raw. A circle of black hair covered the only surface that had not been cooked. From a distance it looked like he was wearing a cooking pot. He and Dr. Chodo were near the Asano Sentei Park when the explosion occurred. Before the day was out Dr. Harada died, and his wife's family took his corpse to their home in Kabe.

Dr. Okura, another of our dentists, went out this morning to look for his wife, missing since the day of the bombing. He returned later with some bones that he picked up where she had been last seen. Mr. Yamazaki, in the business office, was still trying to find his daughter, but without success. Dr. Fujii finally found his daughter, but she was beyond help. She died in a friend's house in Midorii.

There was to be no more good news today. Dr. Morisugi, in our Internal Medical Department, was still missing, and since he had lived near the center of the explosion, we assumed that he and his entire family were killed. Three of our nurses had been killed and Miss Hinada, who seemed to be all right before her diarrhea started, was dying.

Towards evening, the young officer died whom I had heard begging for water last night. His mother, coming all the way from Yamaguchi Prefecture, found him a few minutes after he had drawn his last breath.

A little girl was given the young officer's bed in the isolation ward. Her cries for her mother were heartbreaking.

Darkness came, and still there were no lights except the lights from the fires where the dead were burned. And again, the smell of burning flesh. The hospital was quieter, but in the isolation ward the stillness of the night was broken again and again by the little girl.

"Mother," she would cry, "it hurts! I can't stand it. *Eraiyo!*"

Not until the eastern sky began to brighten did I fall into troubled sleep.

1955

THE FUTURE OF MANKIND

BERTRAND RUSSELL

Before the end of the present century, unless something quite unforseeable occurs, one of three possibilities will have been realized. These three are:

I. The end of human life, perhaps of all life on our planet.
II. A reversion to barbarism after a catastrophic diminution of the population of the globe.
III. A unification of the world under a single government, possessing a monopoly of all the major weapons of war.

I do not pretend to know which of these will happen, or even which is the most likely. What I do contend, without any hesitation, is that the kind of system to which we have been accustomed cannot possibly continue.

The first possibility, the extinction of the human race, is not to be expected in the next world war, unless that war is postponed for a longer time than now seems probable. But if the next world war is indecisive, or if the victors are unwise, and if organized states survive it, a period of feverish technical development may be expected to follow its conclusion. With vastly more powerful means of utilizing atomic energy than those now available, it is thought by many sober men of science that radioactive clouds, drifting round the world, may disintegrate living tissue everywhere. Although the last survivor may proclaim himself universal Emperor, his reign will be brief and his subjects will all be corpses. With his death the uneasy episode of life will end, and the peaceful rocks will revolve unchanged until the sun explodes.

Perhaps a disinterested spectator would consider this the most desirable consummation, in view of man's long record of folly and cruelty. But we, who are actors in the drama, who are entangled in the net of private affections and public hopes, can hardly take this attitude with any sincerity. True, I have heard men say that they would prefer the end of man to submission to the Soviet government, and doubtless in Russia there are those who would say the same about submission to Western capitalism. But this is rhetoric with a bogus air of heroism. Although it must be regarded as unimaginative humbug, it is dangerous, because it makes men less energetic in seeking ways of avoiding the catastrophe that they pretend not to dread.

The second possibility, that of a reversion to barbarism, would leave open the likelihood of a gradual return to civilization, as after the fall of Rome. The sudden transition will, if it occurs, be infinitely painful to those who experience it, and for some centuries afterwards life will be hard and drab. But at any rate there will still be a future for mankind, and the possibility of rational hope.

I think such an outcome of a really scientific world war is by no means improbable. Imagine each side in a position to destroy the chief cities and centers of industry of the enemy; imagine an almost complete obliteration of laboratories and libraries, accompanied by a heavy casualty rate among men of science; imagine famine due to radioactive spray, and pestilence caused by bacteriological warfare: would social cohesion survive such strains? Would not prophets tell the maddened populations that their ills were wholly due to science, and that the extermination of all educated men would bring the millennium? Extreme hopes are born of extreme misery, and in such a world hopes could only be irrational. I think the great states to which we are accustomed would break up, and the sparse survivors would revert to a primitive village economy.

The third possibility, that of the establishment of a single government for the whole world, might be realized in various ways: by the victory of the United States in the next world war, or by the victory of the U.S.S.R., or, theoretically, by agreement. Or—and I think this is the most hopeful of the issues that are in any degree probable—by an alliance of the nations that desire an international government, becoming, in the end, so strong that Russia would no longer dare to stand out. This might conceivably be achieved without another world war, but it would require courageous and imaginative statesmanship in a number of countries.

There are various arguments that are used against the project of a single government of the whole world. The commonest is that the project is utopian and impossible. Those who use this argument, like most of those who advocate a world government, are thinking of a world government brought about by agreement. I think it is plain that the mutual suspicions between Russia and the West make it futile to hope, in any near future, for any genuine agreement. Any pretended universal authority to which both sides can agree, as things stand, is bound to be a sham, like U.N.O. Consider the difficulties that have been encountered in the much more modest project of an international control over atomic energy, to which Russia will only consent if inspection is subject to the veto, and therefore a farce. I think we should admit that a world government will have to be imposed by force.

But—many people will say—why all this talk about a world government? Wars have occurred ever since men were organized into units larger than the family, but the human race has survived. Why should it not continue to survive even if wars go on occurring from time to time? Moreover, people like war, and will feel frustrated without it. And without war there will be no adequate opportunity for heroism or self-sacrifice.

This point of view—which is that of innumerable elderly gentlemen, including the rulers of Soviet Russia—fails to take account of modern technical possibilities. I think civilization could probably survive one more world war, provided it occurs fairly soon and does not last long. But if there is no slowing up in the rate of discovery and invention, and if great wars continue to recur, the destruction to be expected, even if it fails to exterminate the human race, is pretty certain to produce the kind of reversion to a primitive social system that I spoke of a moment ago. And this will entail such an enormous diminution of population, not only by war, but by subsequent starvation and disease, that the survivors are bound to be fierce and, at least for a considerable time, destitute of the qualities required for rebuilding civilization.

Nor is it reasonable to hope that, if nothing drastic is done, wars will nevertheless not occur. They always have occurred from time to time, and obviously will break out again sooner or later unless mankind adopt some system that makes them impossible. But the only such system is a single government with a monopoly of armed force.

If things are allowed to drift, it is obvious that the bickering between Russia and the Western democracies will continue until Russia has a considerable store of atomic bombs, and that when that time comes there will be an atomic war. In such a war, even if the worst consequences are avoided, Western Europe, including Great Britain, will be virtually exterminated. If America and the U.S.S.R. survive as organized states, they will presently fight again. If one side is victorious, it will rule the world, and a unitary government of mankind will have come into existence; if not, either mankind, or at least civilization, will perish. This is what must happen if nations and their rulers are lacking in constructive vision.

When I speak of "constructive vision," I do not mean merely the theoretical realization that a world government is desirable. More than half the American nation, according to the Gallup poll, hold this opinion. But most of its advocates think of it as something to be established by friendly negotiation, and shrink from any suggestion of the use of force. In this I think they are mistaken. I am sure that force, or the threat of force, will be necessary. I hope the threat of force may suffice, but, if not, actual force should be employed.

Assuming a monopoly of armed force established by the victory of one side in a war between the U.S. and the U.S.S.R., what sort of world will result?

In either case, it will be a world in which successful rebellion will be impossible. Although, of course, sporadic assassination will still be liable to occur, the concentration of all important weapons in the hands of the victors will make them irresistible, and there will therefore be secure peace. Even if the dominant nation is completely devoid of altruism, its leading inhabitants, at least, will achieve a very high level of material comfort, and will be freed from the tyranny of fear. They are likely, therefore, to become gradually more good-natured and less inclined to persecute. Like the Romans, they will, in the course of time, extend citizenship to the vanquished. There will then be a true world state, and it will be possible to forget that it will have owed its origin to conquest. Which of us, during the reign of Lloyd George, felt humiliated by the contrast with the days of Edward I?

A world empire of either the U.S. or the U.S.S.R. is therefore preferable to the results of a continuation of the present international anarchy.

There are, however, important reasons for preferring a victory of America. I am not contending that capitalism is better than Communism; I think it not impossible that, if America were Communist and Russia were capitalist, I should still be on the side of America. My reason for siding with America is that there is in that country more respect than in Russia for the things that I value in a civilized way of life. The things I have in mind are such as: freedom of thought, freedom of inquiry, freedom of discussion, and humane feeling. What a victory of Russia would mean is easily to be seen in Poland. There were flourishing universities in Poland, containing men of great intellectual eminence. Some of these men, fortunately, escaped; the rest disappeared. Education is now reduced to learning the formula of Stalinist orthodoxy; it is only open (beyond the elementary stage) to young people whose parents are politically irreproachable, and it does not aim at producing any mental faculty except that of glib repetition of correct shibboleths and quick apprehension of the side that is winning official favor. From such an educational system nothing of intellectual value can result.

Meanwhile the middle class was annihilated by mass deportations, first in 1940, and again after the expulsion of the Germans. Politicians of majority parties were liquidated, imprisoned, or compelled to fly. Betraying friends to the police, or perjury when they were brought to trial, are often the only means of survival for those who have incurred governmental suspicions.

I do not doubt that, if this régime continues for a generation, it will succeed in its objects. Polish hostility to Russia will die out, and be replaced by Communist orthodoxy. Science and philosophy, art and literature, will become sycophantic adjuncts of government, jejune, narrow, and stupid. No individual will think, or even feel, for himself, but each will be contentedly a mere unit in the mass. A victory of Russia would, in time, make such a mentality world-wide. No doubt the complacency induced by success would ultimately lead to a relaxation of control, but the process would be slow, and the revival of respect for the individual would be doubtful. For such reasons I should view a Russian victory as an appalling disaster.

A victory by the United States would have far less drastic consequences. In the first place, it would not be a victory of the United States in isolation, but of an Alliance in which the other members would be able to insist upon retaining a large part of their traditional independence. One can hardly imagine the American army seizing the dons at Oxford and Cambridge and sending them to hard labor in Alaska. Nor do I think that they would accuse Mr. Attlee of plotting and compel him to fly to Moscow. Yet these are strict analogues to the things the Russians have done in Poland. After a victory of an Alliance led by the United States there would still be British culture, French culture, Italian culture, and (I hope) German culture; there would not, therefore, be the same dead uniformity as would result from Soviet domination.

There is another important difference, and that is that Moscow orthodoxy is much more all-pervasive than that of Washington. In America, if you are a geneticist, you may hold whatever view of Mendelism the evidence makes you regard as the most probable; in Russia, if you are a geneticist who disagrees with Lysenko, you are liable to disappear mysteriously. In America, you may write a book debunking Lincoln if you feel so disposed; in Russia, if you write a book debunking Lenin, it would not be published and you would be liquidated. If you are an American economist, you may hold, or not hold, that America is heading for a slump; in Russia, no economist dare question that an American slump is imminent. In America, if you are a professor of philosophy, you may be an idealist, a materialist, a pragmatist, a logical positivist, or whatever else may take your fancy; at congresses you can argue with men whose opinions differ from yours, and listeners can form a judgment as to who has the best of it. In Russia you must be a dialectical materialist, but at one time the element of materialism outweighs the element of dialectic, and at other times it is the other way round. If you fail to follow the developments of official metaphysics with sufficient nimbleness, it will be the worse for you. Stalin at all times knows the truth about metaphysics, but you must not suppose that the truth this year is the same as it was last year.

In such a world intellect must stagnate, and even technological progress must soon come to an end.

Liberty, of the sort that Communists despise, is im-

portant not only to intellectuals or to the more fortunate sections of society. Owing to its absence in Russia, the Soviet government has been able to establish a
greater degree of economic inequality than exists in
Great Britain, or even in America. An oligarchy
which controls all the means of publicity can perpe-
trate injustices and cruelties which would be scarcely
possible if they were widely known. Only democracy
and free publicity can prevent the holders of power
from establishing a servile state, with luxury for the
few and overworked poverty for the many. This is
what is being done by the Soviet government wherever
it is in secure control. There are, of course, economic
inequalities everywhere, but in a democratic régime
they tend to diminish, whereas under an oligarchy they
tend to increase. And wherever an oligarchy has power,
economic inequalities threaten to become permanent
owing to the modern impossibility of successful rebellion.

I come now to the question: what should be our
policy, in view of the various dangers to which mankind is exposed? To summarize the above arguments:
We have to guard against three dangers: (1) the extinction of the human race; (2) a reversion to barbarism; (3) the establishment of a universal slave
state, involving misery for the vast majority, and the
disappearance of all progress in knowledge and
thought. Either the first or second of these disasters is
almost certain unless great wars can soon be brought to
an end. Great wars can only be brought to an end by
the concentration of armed force under a single au-

thority. Such a concentration cannot be brought about by agreement, because of the opposition of Soviet Russia, but it must be brought about somehow.

The first step—and it is one which is now not very difficult—is to persuade the United States and the British Commonwealth of the absolute necessity for a military unification of the world. The governments of the English-speaking nations should then offer to all other nations the option of entering into a firm Alliance, involving a pooling of military resources and mutual defense against aggression. In the case of hesitant nations, such as Italy, great inducements, economic and military, should be held out to produce their cooperation.

At a certain stage, when the Alliance had acquired sufficient strength, any Great Power still refusing to join should be threatened with outlawry, and, if recalcitrant, should be regarded as a public enemy. The resulting war, if it occurred fairly soon, would probably leave the economic and political structure of the United States intact, and would enable the victorious Alliance to establish a monopoly of armed force, and therefore to make peace secure. But perhaps, if the Alliance were sufficiently powerful, war would not be necessary, and the reluctant Powers would prefer to enter it as equals rather than, after a terrible war, submit to it as vanquished enemies. If this were to happen, the world might emerge from its present dangers without another great war. I do not see any hope of such a happy issue by any other method. But whether Russia would yield when threatened with war is a question as to which I do not venture an opinion.

I have been dealing mainly with the gloomy aspects of the present situation of mankind. It is necessary to do so, in order to persuade the world to adopt measures running counter to traditional habits of thought and ingrained prejudices. But beyond the difficulties and probable tragedies of the near future there is the possibility of immeasurable good, and of greater well-being than has ever before fallen to the lot of man. This is not merely a possibility, but, if the Western democracies are firm and prompt, a probability. From the break-up of the Roman Empire to the present day, states have almost continuously increased in size. There are now only two fully independent states, America and Russia. The next step in this long historical process should reduce the two to one, and thus put an end to the period of organized wars, which began in Egypt some 6,000 years ago. If war can be prevented without the establishment of a grinding tyranny, a weight will be lifted from the human spirit, deep collective fears will be exorcised, and as fear diminishes we may hope that cruelty also will grow less.

The uses to which men have put their increased control over natural forces are curious. In the nineteenth century they devoted themselves chiefly to increasing the numbers of *homo sapiens,* particularly of the white variety. In the twentieth century they have, so far, pursued the exactly opposite aim. Owing to the increased productivity of labor, it has become possible to devote a larger percentage of the population to war. If atomic energy were to make production easier, the only effect, as things are, would be to make wars worse, since fewer people would be needed for producing necessaries. Unless we can cope with the problem of abolishing war, there is no reason whatever to rejoice in labor-saving technique, but quite the reverse. On the other hand, if the danger of war were removed, scientific technique could at last be used to promote human happiness. There is no longer any technical reason for the persistence of poverty, even in such densely populated countries as India and China. If war no longer occupied men's thoughts and energies, we could, within a generation, put an end to all serious poverty throughout the world.

I have spoken of liberty as a good, but it is not an absolute good. We all recognize the need to restrain murderers, and it is even more important to restrain murderous states. Liberty must be limited by law, and its most valuable forms can only exist within a framework of law. What the world most needs is effective laws to control international relations. The first and most difficult step in the creation of such law is the establishment of adequate sanctions, and this is only possible through the creation of a single armed force in control of the whole world. But such an armed force, like a municipal police force, is not an end in itself; it is a means to the growth of a social system governed by law, where force is not the prerogative of private individuals or nations, but is exercised only by a neutral authority in accordance with rules laid down in advance. There is hope that law, rather than private force, may come to govern the relations of nations within the present century. If this hope is not realized we face utter disaster; if it is realized, the world will be far better than at any previous period in the history of man.

1950

AMERICAN HERITAGE SHORT HISTORY OF THE CIVIL WAR

BY BRUCE CATTON

A concise presentation of the Civil War by its most famous living student. This fast moving narrative covers both the political and military aspects of the war and succeeds in capturing the feelings of a nation during the years of its greatest peril.

Here too is the ordinary soldier who, speaking for all America, North and South, says something this country can never forget.

LAUREL LEAF LIBRARY   50c